# Union des grands crus de Bordeaux

# GREAT BORDEAUX: CONSTANT EVOLUTION

Olivier Bernard
President of the Union des Grands Crus de Bordeaux

Going back several hundred years, the long history of our estates has helped us to reflect the infinite complexity of our terroirs, generation after generation.

Today's great wines are as different from those of the 1980s as the latter were from their counterparts of the 1950s. And one could make similar comparisons going back much further...

In addition, the next thirty vintages will undoubtedly be marked by a degree of precision winemaking never before attained in our vineyards and cellars, giving an added dimension.

The one hundred thirty four châteaux belonging to the Union des Grands Crus are all passionate about the unique personality of their wines. They are thus delighted to discuss and share this convivial time with you.

I wish you an excellent tasting.

# BORDEAUX, THE WINE CAPITAL

Alain Juppé
Mayor of Bordeaux
President of Bordeaux Métropole

Bordeaux welcomed some 6 million French and foreign visitors in 2014, 56% of whom came for wine tourism. These record figures illustrate how attractive the city has become.

Among Bordeaux's many advantages, two have especially contributed to the city's growth and fame: its location on the Garonne River and its fine wine.

Major urban development programmes have changed the face of the city and put its citizens back in touch with the river. Entirely renovated on a stretch more than 4 kilometres long, the quays have now come alive with thousands of people enjoying a walk along the waterfront or taking part in celebrations. It was thus only natural that we should decide to organise the Bordeaux Wine Festival there two years ago. This was a resounding success. For four days, hundreds of thousands of people gathered on the quays to enjoy good food and wine, as well as the warm, friendly atmosphere. The Wine Festival has become a factor in Bordeaux's international impact, spawning similar events in Quebec City, Brussels, and Hong Kong to enable producers to display their wines and expertise.

The indissoluble links between Bordeaux and wine are epitomised by Vinexpo, a leading trade fair that attracts professionals from five continents.

In 2016, Bordeaux will also have a new, long-awaited facility to assert its role as wine capital: the Cité du Vin, built in conjunction with the wine industry and located at the entrance to the Port of Bordeaux. This location is a reminder of times past when countless ships sailed down the Garonne with their holds full of barrels, contributing enormously to the city's prosperity.

# The Cité du Vin

Sylvie Cazes
President of the Foundation for the
Culture and Civilisations of Wine

The goal of the Foundation for the Culture and Civilisations of Wine is to promote and share the global culture and living heritage of wine with the greatest number of people.

Blessed with an international reputation and an outstanding image thanks to the fine wine with which it is associated, Bordeaux has become one of Europe's top tourist destinations.

In keeping with this development, The Cité du Vin, under the aegis of our foundation, will open in Bordeaux in June 2016. The Cité fits in perfectly with the history of our city, intimately linked with that of wine. This major cultural institution with nearly 14,000 m² of floor space will unquestionably become one of the city's major drawing cards. Some 450,000 visitors are expected.

The Cité du Vin will offer a trip through time and space to discover the world's wine civilisations. All year long, visitors will be able to take advantage of a permanent, interactive, multi-sensory tour, as well as a rich and varied cultural programme, not to mention international art exhibitions, performances, special events, and tastings of all kinds.

This cultural programme will be made possible thanks to sponsors in France and abroad, as was the construction of the building, partially financed by some 70 patrons.

We are proud that the Union des Grands Crus de Bordeaux has been by our side since 2013 as a *Bâtisseur d'Honneur* of the Cité du Vin.

# THE GIRONDINS: A STATE OF MIND

Jean-Louis Triaud
President of the Girondins de Bordeaux

Bordeaux is famous around the world for its wines and impressive châteaux.

The Girondins football team has also defended the name and values of Bordeaux in France and Europe Since 1881. The Club des Girondins was elected the most serious and most appreciated by French football supporters in 2015. With a background of over two hundred European matches, the Girondins have helped to spread the city's reputation far and wide, and the team is, in fact, the second thing that comes to mind when people hear the name "Bordeaux".

Located at the gateway to the city, near the Médoc, the new stadium is already a source a great pride to the region thanks to its beautiful architecture incorporating various references to Bordeaux, as well as the nearby countryside, vineyards, ocean, and forest.

Combining modernity and tradition, elegance and festiveness, the stadium will undoubtedly provide a natural link between actors of the local economy.

# VINEXPO

## Xavier de Eizaguirre
## President of Vinexpo

The world wine market remains dynamic, with constantly growing consumption. However, there are many contrasts and changes in consumer purchasing habits. The transformations are major and uncertainties numerous.

This leads us to adapt, rethink our strategies, discover new opportunities, strengthen our leadership, and open up new markets.

In this context, Vinexpo, the international wine and spirits fair, remains an important partner to the wine industry. An essential platform to develop business and enlarge distribution, Vinexpo has set the standard in Bordeaux, Hong Kong, and Tokyo.

Bringing together the wine trade on five continents, and featuring the world's most famous wines, Vinexpo is an essential meeting place for producers, merchants, importers, distributors, and sommeliers.

The tasting of the Union des Grands Crus is unquestionably one of the high points of each and every Vinexpo.

# List by Appellation

# Château Cheval Blanc

## Premier Grand Cru Classé «A»

## Background

Once upon a time, Cheval Blanc was a modest tenant farm (that nevertheless had a long winegrowing history) called Le Barrail des Cailloux. However, starting in the 19th century, the estate took on an aura of romanticism and greatness. From the time the château was created in 1834 until its present-day boundaries were fixed in 1871, Cheval Blanc became a legend.

Since it takes two parents to have children, it can be said that Cheval Blanc was born of the marriage between Merlot, the traditional grape variety in Saint-Émilion and Pomerol, and Cabernet Franc.
Helped by the fact that phylloxera spared the estate in the late 19th century, the château's reputation grew and grew. In fact, the wine was in strong demand in port cities and trading posts around the world... London, Paris, Antwerp, etc. The 20th century brought truly international recognition.

In 1954, Cheval Blanc was classified a Premier Grand Cru Classé A, and this supreme distinction has been confirmed in every subsequent classification.

## A special spirit

Since 1998, Bernard Arnault and Baron Frère have perpetuated Cheval Blanc's tradition of excellence, while introducing elegant modern influences. Baron Frère is a member of the board of directors of some of the most powerful financial and industrial groups in Europe. A true connoisseur, he is passionate, respectful and curious about fine wine.

As for Bernard Arnault, his name is forever linked with that of LVMH, the world's leading luxury goods group, with such fabulous brands as Dior, Krug, Moët-Hennessy, Louis Vuitton, and Château d'Yquem. By serving Cheval Blanc to his guests and making sure that it graces fine tables around the world, he added even more lustre to the wine.

# THE FUTURE

Planned for quite some time, the construction of new buildings and a new cellar became a reality in 2011.

The owners of Cheval Blanc wanted to create a "wine workshop" that also makes a strong architectural statement in tune with the 21st century, while reflecting its status as a famous great growth. This challenge was met by the 1994 Pritzker Prize winning architect, Christian de Portzamparc, who designed a winery totally integrated with its surroundings.

Château Cheval Blanc 33330 Saint-Émilion
Tel. +33 (0)5 57 55 55 55 - Fax +33 (0)5 57 55 55 50
contact@chateau-chevalblanc.com - **www.chateau-chevalblanc.com**

# CHÂTEAU MOUTON ROTHSCHILD

## PREMIER GRAND CRU CLASSÉ

Château Mouton Rothschild, a *Premier Cru Classé* since 1973, now belongs to Camille Sereys de Rothschild, Philippe Sereys de Rothschild and Julien de Beaumarchais de Rothschild, the three children of Baroness Philippine de Rothschild and grandchildren of the legendary Baron Philippe. The château is managed by Baron Philippe de Rothschild S.A., the family firm responsible for the viticulture activities. The estate comprises 83 hectares of vines in Pauillac, planted with Cabernet Sauvignon (81%), Merlot (15%), Cabernet Franc (3%) and Petit Verdot (1%), and boasts an exceptional terroir, both for the quality of its soil and its exposure to sunlight. Combining respect for tradition with the latest technology, meticulous care and attention are given from grape to bottle: hand picking, manual and optical sorting, fermentation vats with transparent staves, maturing in new oak barrels, etc.

Château Mouton Rothschild's long, proud history can be summarized in a few key dates.

In 1853, Baron Nathaniel de Rothschild, from the English branch of the family, acquired Château Brane-Mouton, which he renamed Château Mouton Rothschild.

In 1922, his great-grandson, Baron Philippe (1902-1988), took the future of the estate into his own hands. The 65 years of his reign bear the stamp of his strong personality, his spirit of enterprise and his openness to new ideas.

In 1924, he was the first to introduce château bottling.

In 1926, he built the famous *Grand Chai*, the majestic 100-metre great barrel hall that remains a major attraction of the Mouton tour.

1945, the Victory year that concluded the Second World War, heralded the start of an exciting collection of artworks created each year by famous painters for the Mouton label.

1962 saw the inauguration of the Museum of Wine in Art. Located next to the Great Barrel Hall, it contains a collection of precious objects devoted to the vine and wine spanning three millennia which draws thousands of visitors every year.

In 1988, Baroness Philippine de Rothschild (1933-2014) succeeded her father at the head of the estate, becoming in her turn the guarantor of the quality of this illustrious wine. In 1981, she had already decided to honour the close link between art and wine by creating "Paintings for the Labels", a travelling exhibition devoted to the artists who have illustrated each vintage of Mouton.

In 1991, she created Aile d'Argent, a white wine made from grapes grown on a few hectares of vines on the Mouton estate planted with Sauvignon Blanc (57%), Sémillon (42%) and Muscadelle (1%).

In 1993, Mouton also began to produce a second wine for the first time: le Petit Mouton de Mouton Rothschild.

In 2013, Baroness Philippine crowned the renovation of Mouton with the inauguration of a new vat room and an exhibition space for "Paintings for the Labels", now permanently on display in the heart of the estate.

2014: Philippe Sereys de Rothschild succeeded his mother as Chairman of the Supervisory Board of Baron Philippe de Rothschild S.A. He had been Vice Chairman since 2006. Following in his mother's and grandfather's footsteps and in close collaboration with his sister and his brother, he is determined to continue to enhance the quality and reputation of this family-owned First Growth.

President of the Supervisory Board of Baron Philippe de Rothschild S.A. : Philippe Sereys de Rothschild
Managing Director: Philippe Dhalluin
Technical Director: Erick Tourbier
Commercial Director: Hervé Gouin

Château Mouton Rothschild BP 117 - 33250 Pauillac
Tel. +33 (0)5 56 73 20 20 - Fax +33 (0)5 56 73 20 33
visites@bphr.com - www.chateau-mouton-rothschild.com

# Château d'Yquem

## Premier Cru Supérieur Classé en 1855

Dating back to the 15th century, an impressive manor house – more of a fortified farm than a château – overlooks the Sauternes countryside from a hill forty kilometres south of the city of Bordeaux.

This building was famous as long ago as the Enlightenment. Its name: Château d'Yquem.

The wine, a miracle of nature, owes its exquisite quality not only to a unique terroir and the professionalism of the Yquem team in the vineyard and the cellar, but also to a microscopic fungus (*Botrytis cinerea*) found in the Sauternes region and especially at Yquem. This divine nectar with a fabulous golden colour is famous from Moscow to Washington, by way of Seoul, London, Hong Kong, Tokyo, etc.

In the autumn, morning mists give way to sunny afternoons. If accompanied by an easterly wind, conditions are just right to send pickers out to harvest the hundred hectares of vines, seeking only the finest Sémillon and Sauvignon Blanc grapes affected by "noble rot," which concentrates both sweetness and flavour.

The sweet, botyrtised gapes are carefully removed with small secateurs in order not to harm the remaining grapes that have not yet reached 20 degrees potential alcohol.

In an average year, pickers go over each vineyard plot six different times – as things have been here done since the 19th century...

The grapes are pressed as soon as they arrive at the cellar and the juice is immediately put into new oak barrels for fermentation.

The wine is then aged in these same barrels for the next thirty months, during which it is regularly topped up and racked.

Since 1999, the L.V.M.H (Moët Hennessy - Louis Vuitton) group have been majority shareholders of this estate rated a Premier Cru Supérieur in the 1855 classification, and Pierre Lurton is the manager.

Yquem's philosophy has been the same for the past five centuries: to cooperate with nature to produce an average of just one glass of this famous wine per vine.

It is extremely rare for the entire crop to be sold under the Château d'Yquem name, and no Yquem at all is produced in disappointing vintages. Nine vintages were thus not marketed by Yquem in the 20th century, and 2012 is the first one missing in the 21st.

Quality comes at this price!

Managing Director: Pierre Lurton
Technical Director: Francis Mayeur
Cellar Master: Sandrine Garbay - Vineyard Manager: Antoine Depierre

Château d'Yquem - 33210 Sauternes
GPS: Latitude: 44.5445174 - Longitude: -0.3292862
Tel. +33 (0)5 57 98 07 07 - Fax +33 (0)5 57 98 07 08
info@yquem.fr - www.yquem.fr

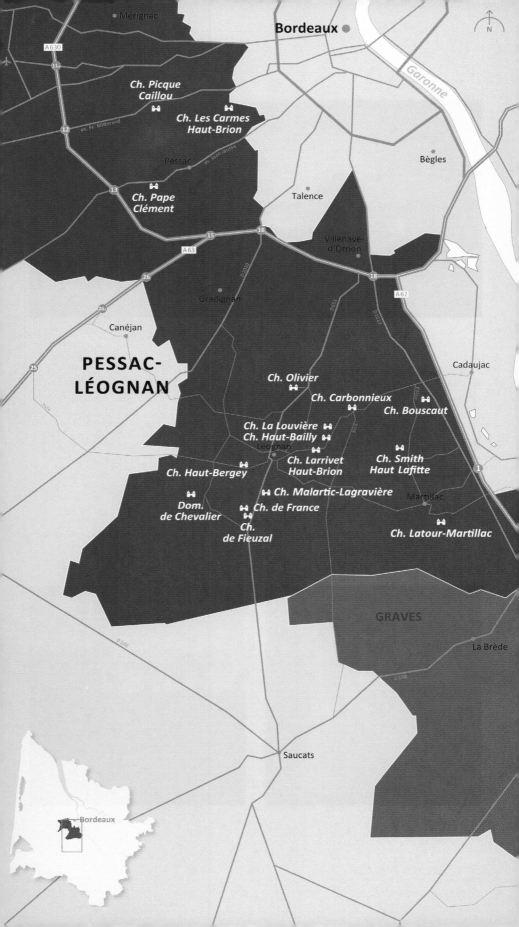

# CRUS DE PESSAC-LÉOGNAN

Although Pessac-Léognan is the youngest appellation in Bordeaux (1987), it is paradoxically the cradle of winegrowing in the Gironde department. From the time they were first planted to the present day, i.e. for some 21 centuries, the vineyards of Pessac-Léognan have contributed to the prestige and development of Bordeaux wine.

The first diocesan records, dating back to 1382, mention wine production here, including the estate belonging to Bertrand de Goth (elected Pope under the name of Clément V in 1305) that was later given to the archbishops of Bordeaux. Since then, many well-known people have lived or stayed in the region. The Black Prince had a hunting lodge in Léognan, and Montesquieu, not only a famous philosopher and author of "The Spirit of Laws", but also a winegrower, was undoubtedly inspired by the wines of the Graves – which also guaranteed him financial independence.

The very notion of cru and production of the first great Bordeaux wines can be traced back to Château Haut-Brion in the late 17th century. This prestigious estate is now in the forefront of the Graves Great Growths, all of which are located in the Pessac-Léognan appellation.

These estates, members of the Union des Grands Crus de Bordeaux, bear witness to an outstanding history.

# CHÂTEAU BOUSCAUT

## CRU CLASSÉ DE GRAVES

*Owners: Sophie Lurton-Cogombles and Laurent Cogombles*

Vines were first planted at Bouscaut, in the commune of Cadaujac, in the 17th century.

The beautiful manor house, adorned with roses, dates from the 18th century and is located 20 minutes from the city of Bordeaux. The château is surrounded by century-old trees and faces the vineyard.

In 1979, Lucien Lurton, a famous Bordeaux winegrower, added Bouscaut to the list of great growth estates he acquired during that decade. Sophie Lurton, his daughter, has managed the estate for the past twenty years with her husband, Laurent Cogombles. Thanks to their unceasing efforts to improve the vineyard in keeping with environmental concerns, their renovation of the vat rooms, and the construction of a new 300 m2 barrel cellar in 2010, Laurent and Sophie Cogombles have given Bouscaut the means to produce great white and red wines. Decorated with barrel staves, the outer walls of the new cellar reflect the philosophy of the owners: integration into the environment and respect for tradition. Château Bouscaut offers numerous workshops to discover the world of Bouscaut and also offers guest accommodation at nearby Château Valoux.

20

| | |
|---|---|
| Area under vine | 42 hectares |
| Production | Red wine: 100,000 bottles - White wine: 20,000 bottles |
| Soil | Gravel and clay on a limestone platform |
| Grape varieties | Red wine: 46% Merlot, 48% Cabernet Sauvignon, 6% Malbec |
| | White wine: 50% Sémillon, 50% Sauvignon Blanc |
| Barrel ageing | Red wine: 18 months - White wine: 12 months - New barrels: 40% |
| Second wine | Les Chênes de Bouscaut |

**Château Bouscaut** 1477, avenue de Toulouse - 33140 Cadaujac
GPS: Latitude: 44.746389 - Longitude: -0.547778
Tel. +33 (0)5 57 83 12 20 - Fax +33 (0)5 57 83 12 21
cb@chateau-bouscaut.com - **www.chateau-bouscaut.com**

# CHÂTEAU CARBONNIEUX
## CRU CLASSÉ DE GRAVES

## PESSAC-LÉOGNAN
*Owner: the Perrin family*

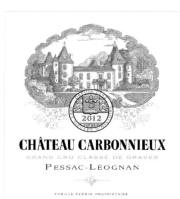

**CHÂTEAU CARBONNIEUX**
GRAND CRU CLASSÉ DE GRAVES
PESSAC-LÉOGNAN

FAMILLE PERRIN PROPRIÉTAIRE

One of the most ancient winegrowing estates in Bordeaux, Château Carbonnieux has made wine without interruption since the 13th century. Built in an understated style, the château itself is an impressive building dating from the Middle Ages.

The first owners – and accomplished winegrowers – were the Benedictine monks of Sainte-Croix abbey in Bordeaux, who made internationally-renowned red and white wines centuries ago. They also succeeded in introducing their pale-coloured, crystalclear white wine to the palace of the Sultan of Constantinople by labelling it "Mineral Water of Carbonnieux" to get around the prohibition against alcoholic beverages...

Carbonnieux has belonged to the Perrin family for three generations.

Located on the highest point in the commune of Léognan, on soil that is perfectly drained by a stream called L'Eau Blanche, Carbonnieux's terroir is especially conducive to producing fine quality red and white wines.

| | |
|---|---|
| Area under vine | 92 hectares |
| Production | Red wine: 200,000 bottles - White wine: 180,000 bottles |
| Soil | Deep gravel on slopes with clay soil |
| Grape varieties | Red wine: 60% Cabernet Sauvignon, 30% Merlot, 7% Cabernet franc, 3% Petit Verdot and Carmenère |
| | White wine: 65% Sauvignon, 35% Sémillon |
| Barrel ageing | Red wine: 15-18 months - White wine: 10 months - New barrels: Red wine: 35-40% - White wine: 30% |
| Second wine | La Croix de Carbonnieux - Château Tour Léognan |

Co-Managers: Éric Perrin and Philibert Perrin

Château Carbonnieux Chemin de Peyssardet 33850 Léognan
GPS: Latitude: 44.745183 - Longitude: -0.566477
Tel. +33 (0)5 57 96 56 20 - Fax +33 (0)5 57 96 59 19
info@chateau-carbonnieux.fr - **www.carbonnieux.com**

# CHÂTEAU LES CARMES HAUT-BRION

Owner: Groupe PICHET

One of the jewels of the Bordeaux wine country, Château Les Carmes Haut-Brion has over 13 hectares of vines. It is in a unique location, an enclave in the city of Bordeaux. In fact, it is the only estate to have vines in the city proper, and the postal address is: 20, rue des Carmes, 33000 Bordeaux. Les Carmes Haut Brion is one of the last "urban" vineyards and is a veritable clos, entirely surrounded by walls.

From 1584 to 1789, Les Carmes Haut Brion belonged to the Carmelite religious order. After the French Revolution, the property was acquired by Bordeaux négociants, the Chantecaille family, and then sold in late 2010 to Groupe Pichet, who were seeking to diversify. They have already planned major investments: restructuring the vineyard as well as building a new cellar for fermenting and ageing the wine.

The château was built in the early 19th century and the three hectares of beautiful grounds designed by the landscape artist Fischer date from the same period. Château Les Carmes Haut Brion is a haven of peace and tranquillity in the historic heart of the Bordeaux wine country. It has an astonishingly warm microclimate that protects the vines from spring frosts and is conducive to early ripening.

| | |
|---|---|
| Area under vine | 13.63 hectares |
| Production | 30,000 bottles |
| Soil | Gravel from the Mindel glaciation on a limestone platform |
| Grape varieties | 45% Merlot, 40% Cabernet franc, 15% Cabernet Sauvignon |
| Barrel ageing | 18-24 months - New barrels 60% |
| Second wine | Le Clos des Carmes Haut-Brion |

Managers: Diane and Patrice Pichet - Director: Guillaume Pouthier - Consultant: Stéphane Derenoncourt

Château Les Carmes Haut-Brion 20 rue des Carmes - 33000 Bordeaux
GPS: Latitude: 44.822493 - Longitude: - 0.610019
Tel. +33 (0)5 56 93 23 40 - Fax +33 (0)5 56 93 10 71
chateau@les-carmes-haut-brion.com - **www.les-carmes-haut-brion.com**

# DOMAINE DE CHEVALIER
## CRU CLASSÉ DE GRAVES

*Owner: S.C. Domaine de Chevalier - the Bernard family*

Located in Léognan, capital of the Graves, Domaine de Chevalier is a very ancient estate. It was designated as "Chibaley" (the Gascon word for chevalier) on the famous 1783 map produced by engineer Pierre de Belleyme.

The fact that Chevalier has never abandoned the name of "domaine" in favour of the more recent appellation "château" is proof of the estate's long history.

In 1983, Domaine de Chevalier was acquired by the Bernard family, leading French producers of industrial alcohol and major Bordeaux wine merchants.

Chevalier has been managed since then by Olivier Bernard, who perpetuates the spirit of harmony and quest for perfection that has long characterized this superb wine.

Domaine de Chevalier rouge is one of the leading wines in the Pessac-Léognan appellation and one of the finest classed growths of Bordeaux. Domaine de Chevalier blanc is recognized as one of the greatest dry white wines in the world.

| | |
|---|---|
| Area under vine | 50 hectares |
| Production | Red wine: 120,000 bottles - White wine: 20,000 bottles |
| Soil | Gravel, with clay-gravel subsoil |
| Grape varieties | Red wine: 63% Cabernet Sauvignon, 30% Merlot, 5% Petit Verdot, 2% Cabernet franc |
| | White wine: 70% Sauvignon Blanc, 30% Sémillon |
| Barrel ageing | Red wine and White wine: 18 months - New barrels: 35% |
| Second wine | L'Esprit de Chevalier |

Administrator: Olivier Bernard - Assistant Manager: Rémi Edange - Technical Director: Thomas Stonestreet

Domaine de Chevalier 102 chemin de Mignoy - 33850 Léognan
GPS: Latitude: 44.719169 - Longitude: -0.631702
Tel. +33 (0)5 56 64 16 16 - Fax +33 (0)5 56 64 18 18
olivierbernard@domainedechevalier.com - **www.domainedechevalier.com**

# CHÂTEAU DE FIEUZAL

## CRU CLASSÉ DE GRAVES

**PESSAC-LÉOGNAN**

*Owners: Brenda and Lochlann Quinn*

GRAND CRU CLASSÉ DE GRAVES

**CHATEAU
DE FIEUZAL**

*Pessac-Léognan*

MIS EN BOUTEILLE AU CHATEAU

The vineyards of Château de Fieuzal are in the Graves area of Bordeaux, the birthplace of winemaking in the region. The estate, which is officially classified as a one of the great "Grand Cru Classé de Graves" vineyards, takes its name from the Fieuzal family, owners of the vineyard until 1851. The property is now owned by Brenda & Lochlann Quinn and it is famous for producing both elegant whites and opulent reds.

The vineyards receive meticulous attention and each individual plot is closely managed in order to make the most of the outstanding terroir.

Talented young Stephen Carrier has been in charge of the new winemaking team since 2007. He is extremely rigorous and very enthusiastic about producing the best possible wine.

The changes that have taken place at Fieuzal are epitomised by the new vat room, with concrete, oak, and stainless steel vats. This ambitious project is now finished and symbolises the estate's quest for finesse and excellence.

24

| | |
|---|---|
| Area under vine | 75 hectares |
| Production | Red wine: 117,000 bottles - White wine: 21,000 bottles |
| Soil | Günz gravel and clay-limestone |
| Grape varieties | Red wine: 48% Cabernet Sauvignon, 45% Merlot, 5% Cabernet franc, 2% Petit Verdot |
| | White wine: 70% Sauvignon blanc, 25% Sémillon, 5% Muscadelle |
| Barrel ageing | Red wine: 14-18 months - White wine: 12-16 months |
| | New barrels: Red wine: 65% - White wine: 40% |
| Second wine | L'Abeille de Fieuzal |

Technical Director: Stephen Carrier

**Château de Fieuzal** 124, avenue de Mont de Marsan - 33850 Léognan
GPS: Latitude: 44.712464 - Longitude: -0.606608
Tel. +33 (0)5 56 64 77 86 - Fax +33 (0)5 56 64 18 88
adenis@fieuzal.com - **www.fieuzal.com**

# CHÂTEAU DE FRANCE

## CHÂTEAU DE FRANCE
### PESSAC-LÉOGNAN
### 2 0 0 9

The vineyard is located on the highest slope of the gravel terrace in Léognan, the tallest of four gravelly terraces deposited by the Garonne River when it overflowed its banks in centuries past. The sunny microclimate and the unusual soil account for Château de France's unique terroir.

The Thomassin family acquired the estate in 1971 and has made numerous investments ever since. The vineyard was entirely replanted and the vat room and cellars renovated. This was all done with one goal in mind: to make very great wine.

Arnaud Thomassin, who came to work at the estate in 1994, is now the manager.

Château de France is distributed in France and around the world. Its fine reputation is an acknowledgement of its quality as well as the major efforts undertaken by the Thomassin family for over forty years.

Both the *grand vin*, Château de France, and the second wine, Château Coquillas, are produced in red and white versions.

| | |
|---|---|
| Area under vine | 41 hectares |
| Production | Red wine: 60,000 bottles - White wine: 18,000 bottles |
| Soil | Deep gravel |
| Grape varieties | Red wine: 55% Cabernet Sauvignon, 45% Merlot - White wine: 80% Sauvignon blanc, 20% Sémillon |
| Barrel ageing | Red wine: 12 months - New barrels: Red wine: 40% |
| Second wine | Château Coquillas |

Managing Director: Arnaud Thomassin

Château de France 98, route de Mont de Marsan - 33850 Léognan
GPS: Latitude: 44.716093 - Longitude: -0.604999
Tel. +33 (0)5 56 64 75 39 - Fax +33 (0)5 56 64 72 13
contact@chateau-de-france.com - **www.chateau-de-france.com**

# CHÂTEAU HAUT-BAILLY

## CRU CLASSÉ DE GRAVES

*Owner: Robert G. Wilmers*

GRAND VIN DE BORDEAUX

### CHATEAU HAUT-BAILLY
#### GRAND CRU CLASSÉ
##### PESSAC-LÉOGNAN
##### 2009

MIS EN BOUTEILLE AU CHATEAU

For over four centuries, Château Haut-Bailly has overlooked a 30 hectare vineyard in a single block entirely devoted to producing red wine.

Haut-Bailly's reputation as one of the great wines of Bordeaux dates from the 19th century, and the word "outstanding" most often associated with the château reflects its superb quality.

Robert G. Wilmers, owner since 1998, and the current manager, Véronique Sanders, have very demanding standards that entail using the best of traditional and modern methods, with full respect for the environment.

A quarter of the vines at Haut-Bailly are a hundred years old, and the estate has a unique terroir that accounts for wines of amazing regularity. These great wines have an inimitable style, finesse, and elegance, whatever the vintage.

| | |
|---|---|
| Area under vine | 30 hectares |
| Production | 80,000 bottles |
| Soil | Sand and gravel |
| Grape varieties | 60% Cabernet Sauvignon, 34% Merlot, 3% Cabernet franc, and 3% Petit Verdot |
| Barrel ageing | 16 months - New barrels: 50-65% |
| Second wine | La Parde Haut-Bailly |

Chief Executive Officer: Véronique Sanders - Technical Director: Gabriel Vialard

Château Haut-Bailly 103, avenue de Cadaujac - 33850 Léognan
GPS: Latitude: 44.73587 - Longitude: -0.580623
Tel. +33 (0)5 56 64 75 11 - Fax +33 (0)5 56 64 53 60
mail@chateau-haut-bailly.com - **www.chateau-haut-bailly.com**

# CHÂTEAU HAUT-BERGEY

## PESSAC-LÉOGNAN

*Owner: Sylviane Garcin*

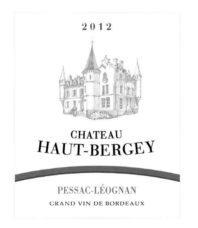

Château Haut-Bergey, with its bartizans topped by conical slate towers, is reminiscent of Sleeping Beauty's castle... an impression reinforced by the pink cellars. The estate dates back to the 15th century. Owner of Haut Bergey since 1991, Sylviane Garcin Cathiard was determined to lavish the same care and attention on her estate as the greatest châteaux in Bordeaux.

This charming property now applies rigorous standards and the necessary technical means to achieve the vineyard's full potential. Soil surveys were done on every plot, enabling each one to receive tailor-made treatment using natural, traditional methods. The grapes are meticulously handpicked and optical sorting retains only perfectly ripe, healthy fruit. Small stainless steel vats are propitious to precision winemaking adapted to grapes from each plot. The ageing cellar houses barrels that are either new or used for one previous vintage. The proportion varies from year to year.

Château Haut-Bergey produces an elegant red wine with fine structure and an outstanding personality, as well as a delicate, elegant white wine.

| | |
|---|---|
| Area under vine | 36 hectares |
| Production | 150,000 bottles |
| Soil | Gravel and clay |
| Grape varieties | Red wine: 45% Merlot noir, 35% Cabernet Sauvignon, 10% Petit Verdot, 7% Cabernet franc, 3% Malbec |
| | White wine: 80% Sauvignon Blanc, 20% Sémillon |
| Barrel ageing | 14-16 months - New barrels: 30% |
| Second wine | Haut-Bergey Cuvée Paul |

President: Sylviane Garcin

Château Haut-Bergey 69, cours Gambetta - BP n°2 - 33850 Léognan
GPS: Latitude: 44.726659 - Longitude: -0.610342
Tel. +33 (0)5 56 64 05 22 - Fax +33 (0)5 56 64 06 98
info@vignoblesgarcin.com - **www.chateauhautbergey.com**

# CHÂTEAU LARRIVET HAUT-BRION

**PESSAC-LÉOGNAN**    *Owner: Philippe Gervoson*

Château Larrivet Haut-Brion was cited as one of the leading wines in the commune of Léognan as early as 1840.

The Gervoson family acquired the estate in 1987 and have worked hard ever since to restore this wine's illustrious reputation.

Spread over a hundred hectares, Larrivet Haut-Brion presently has 75 hectares of vines, as well as 13 hectares of grounds, woods, and meadows.

An ambitious modernisation programme in the cellar (pneumatic winepress using inert gas, optical sorting of grapes, etc.) and vineyard (detailed soil survey for improved plot-by-plot management) has resulted in wines reputed for their elegance and character.

Representing the upcoming generation of her family, Émilie Gervoson tirelessly works towards enhancing Château Larrivet Haut-Brion and promoting the wine around the world.

28

| | |
|---|---|
| Area under vine | 75 hectares |
| Production | Red wine: 150,000 bottles - White wine: 20,000 bottles |
| Soil | Gravel with a clay or sand matrix |
| Grape varieties | Red wine: 50% Merlot, 45% Cabernet Sauvignon, 5% Cabernet franc |
| | White wine: 80% Sauvignon, 20% Sémillon |
| Barrel ageing | Red wine: 16 months - White wine: 11 months - New barrels: Red wine: 33% - White wine: 50% |
| Second wine | Demoiselles de Larrivet Haut-Brion |

Managing Director: Bruno Lemoine - Marketing and public relations: Émilie Gervoson

Château Larrivet Haut-Brion 84, avenue de Cadaujac - 33850 Léognan
GPS: Latitude: 44.731229 - Longitude: -0.585210
Tel. +33 (0)5 56 64 75 51 - Fax +33 (0)5 56 64 53 47
secretariat@larrivethautbrion.fr

# CHÂTEAU LaTOUR-MARTILLAC

## CRU CLASSÉ DE GRAVES

**PESSAC-LÉOGNAN**
*Owner: the Jean Kressmann family*

Designated a Graves classed growth in 1953, Château LaTour-Martillac owes its name to the tower in the courtyard, the vestige of a fortress built in the 12th century by the ancestors of the famous winegrower and philosopher, Montesquieu.

Located on an outstanding rise of Pyrenean gravel, this estate caught the eye of Édouard Kressmann, a Bordeaux négociant, as early as 1871. He was particularly impressed with the quality of the white wines.

His elder son, Alfred, finally bought the estate in 1930. He expanded the red wine vineyard and designed with his son, Jean, the label with gold and sandcoloured diagonal stripes that is still used today. In 1937, the wines of Château LaTour Martillac were honoured at a solemn Coronation Dinner for George VI of England.

Today, Jean Kressmann's sons, Tristan and Loïc, assisted by the best consulting oenologists in Bordeaux, perpetuate the family tradition and always give priority to quality rather than quantity

Thanks to their elegant structure and balance, the red and white wines of LaTour-Martillac (both of which are classed) are widely recognized as among the most reliable in Pessac-Léognan. Like all the great wines from this appellation, the red wines of LaTour Martillac are balanced and elegant. The white wines are surprisingly delicate, complex, and astonishingly long-lived.

| | |
|---|---|
| Area under vine | 50 hectares |
| Production | Red wine: 150,000 bottles - White wine: 36,000 bottles |
| Soil | Pyrenean gravel |
| Grape varieties | Red wine: 60% Cabernet Sauvignon, 35% Merlot, 5% Petit Verdot |
| | White wine: 60% Sauvignon, 40% Sémillon |
| Barrel ageing | Red wine: 14-18 months - White wine: 15 months |
| Second wine | Lagrave-Martillac |

Managing Director: Tristan Kressmann - Technical Director: Loïc Kressmann

Château LaTour-Martillac 8, chemin de la Tour - 33650 Martillac
GPS: Latitude: 44.71 - Longitude: -0.538889
Tel. +33 (0)5 57 97 71 11 - Fax +33 (0)5 57 97 71 17
chateau@latourmartillac.com - **www.latourmartillac.com**

29

# Château La Louvière

*Owner: S.A.S. Les Vignobles André Lurton*

2013

## CHÂTEAU
## LA LOUVIÈRE
PESSAC-LÉOGNAN

*Grand Vin de Bordeaux*
*Mis en bouteille au Château*
ANDRÉ LURTON PROPRIÉTAIRE

Located fourteen kilometres south of the city of Bordeaux, in the heart of the Pessac-Léognan appellation, Château La Louvière's history goes back seven centuries. Records show that wine was already made here in 1310.

However, the vineyard as we know it today dates from the early 16th century. In 1620, the Carthusian monks who inherited the estate contributed their experience and expertise to producing wines that acquired an international reputation.

In 1791, Jean-Baptiste Mareilhac, a rich négociant, purchased the property during the French Revolution and built the present-day château in a pure neoclassical style. It is now a listed historic monument.

André Lurton became the owner of La Louvière in 1965 and has worked tirelessly to restore the estate's former splendour. Christine Lurton-de Caix became La Louvière's ambassadress in 2014 in the context of Vignobles André Lurton's Grands Crus division.

Terroir-based vineyard management, environmentally-friendly viticultural practices, and traditional winemaking methods coupled with the judicious use of modern techniques enable La Louvière to produce dry white and red wines of great character.

| | |
|---|---|
| Area under vine | 61 hectares |
| Production | Red wine: 150,000 bottles - White wine: 60,000 bottles |
| Soil | Gravel and silica with limestone at the bottom of the slope |
| Grape varieties | Red wine: 64% Cabernet Sauvignon, 33% Merlot, and 3% Cabernet Franc |
| | White wine: 85% Sauvignon, 15% Sémillon |
| Barrel ageing | Red wine: 12-18 months - White wine: 9-10 months - New barrels: Red wine: 50% - White wine: 30% |
| Second wine | L de La Louvière |

Managing Director: Pascal Le Faucheur - Consultant oenologist (white wines): Denis Dubourdieu
Consultant oenologist (red wines): Michel Rolland

Château La Louvière 149, avenue de Cadaujac - 33850 Léognan
GPS: Latitude: 44.7360925 - Longitude: -0.5778971
Tel. +33 (0)5 56 64 75 87 - Fax +33 (0)5 56 64 71 76
lalouviere@andrelurton.com - **www.andrelurton.com**

# CHÂTEAU MALARTIC-LAGRAVIÈRE

## CRU CLASSÉ DE GRAVES

PESSAC-LÉOGNAN        *Owner: Alfred-Alexandre Bonnie*

GRAND CRU CLASSÉ
PESSAC-LÉOGNAN

Originally named "Domaine de la Gravière", this estate is located in Bordeaux's most ancient winegrowing district. The vines grow on one of the region's most beautiful gravelly rises, consisting of alluvial deposits left millions of years ago.

The Maurès family acquired Domaine de la Gravière in the late 18th century, and it was later renamed Malartic-Lagravière in honour of Hippolyte, Count de Malartic, a famous admiral in the royal navy.

The estate was acquired by Michèle and Alfred-Alexandre Bonnie in late 1996. They completely renovated the 53 hectares of vines, including 7 of white wine grapes. Designed around the gravity flow concept, the chateau's impressive state-of-the-art vat room is used to make wine based on traditional principles.

The estate has a magnificent gravel and clay terroir, and the vines are tended with meticulous care. The soil is ploughed all year long and work in the vineyard is done according to the precepts of sustainable agriculture.

Malartic-Lagravière is one of just six Bordeaux châteaux that produce both red and white classified growths. The intense, complex and elegant wines are famous the world over and are served in the best restaurants and at the finest tables.

| | |
|---|---|
| Area under vine | 53 hectares |
| Production | 230,000 bottles |
| Soil | Dry gravel and clay gravel |
| Grape varieties | Red wine: 45% Cabernet Sauvignon, 45% Merlot, 8% Cabernet franc, 2% Petit Verdot |
| | White wine: 80% Sauvignon, 20% Sémillon |
| Barrel ageing | Red wine: 15-22 months - White wine: 10-15 months - New barrels: 40-70% |
| Second wine | La Réserve de Malartic |

Vice-presidents: Véronique Bonnie-Laplane and Jean-Jacques Bonnie
Cellar Master: Philippe Garcia - Vineyard Manager: Benoît Prévoteau

Château Malartic-Lagravière 43, avenue de Mont de Marsan - 33850 Léognan
GPS: Latitude: 44.7245035 - Longitude: -0,6002992
Tel. +33 (0)5 56 64 75 08 - Fax +33 (0)5 56 64 99 66
malartic-lagraviere@malartic-lagraviere.com - **www.malartic-lagraviere.com**

# CHÂTEAU OLIVIER

## CRU CLASSÉ DE GRAVES

*Owner: the Jean-Jacques de Bethmann family*

**Château Olivier**
Grand Cru Classé
PESSAC-LÉOGNAN

Château Olivier emerges in a vast clearing in the middle of a large estate consisting of forest, meadows, and vines. The château's distinctive architecture, ponds, attractive outbuildings, and beautiful natural setting just eleven kilometres from the city of Bordeaux make this an outstanding property.

Olivier is a very ancient seigneury, whose history goes back to the early Middle Ages, and it is said that the Black Prince (the eldest son of King Edward III of England) liked to hunt here. The estate has belonged to the de Bethmann family since the 19th century.

They have invested heavily in renovating the estate in recent years. A detailed soil survey has revealed new potential for the terroir and led to the same vineyard configuration as in the 18th century. Six different grape varieties are grown on gravelly soil atop clay-limestone bedrock. These are all picked by hand into small crates and sorted first in the vineyard and again in the cellar.

Château Olivier was classified in 1953 for both its red and white wines.

32

| | |
|---|---|
| Area under vine | 60 hectares |
| Production | Red wine: 120,000 bottles - White wine: 30,000 bottles |
| Soil | Deep, compact gravel on marl, clay, and limestone from the Miocene epoch |
| Grape varieties | Red wine: 50% Cabernet Sauvignon, 48% Merlot, 2% Petit Verdot |
| | White wine: 70% Sauvignon Blanc, 28% Sémillon, 2% Muscadelle |
| Barrel ageing | 12 months - New barrels: 35% |
| Second wine | Le Dauphin d'Olivier - La Seigneurerie d'Olivier |

Manager: Alexandre de Bethmann - Managing Director: Laurent Lebrun - Technical Director: Philippe Stoeckle
Commercial and marketing: Estelle Mirieu de Labarre

Château Olivier 175 avenue de Bordeaux - 33850 Martillac
GPS: Latitude: 44.74975 - Longitude: - 0.588485
Tel. +33 (0)5 56 64 73 31 - Fax +33 (0)5 56 64 54 23
mail@chateau-olivier.com - **www.chateau-olivier.com**

# CHÂTEAU PAPE CLÉMENT

## CRU CLASSÉ DE GRAVES

*Owner: Bernard Magrez*

Few great wines can boast seven centuries of history and trace their origins back to a pope. Elected supreme pontiff during the reign of King Philip the Handsome in 1305, Clement V gave his name to Château Pape Clément.

The present owner does his utmost to perpetuate the ancient tradition of quality. Among other innovations, this was the first estate in Bordeaux to destem the entire crop by hand. The grapes are transported by gravity flow into small oak fermentation vats adapted to the yield of each plot. The entire winemaking process is conducted with minute attention to detail. Combining traditional and state-of-the-art techniques, Pape Clément is made according to the highest standards.

Everything is done in the vineyard to let the terroir express itself fully. As part of an environmentally-friendly approach, chemical weed killers have been abandoned in favour of ploughing.

| | |
|---|---|
| Area under vine | 60 hectares |
| Production | Red wine: 110,000 bottles - White wine: 10,000 bottles |
| Soil | Pyrenean clay gravel from the late Pliocene and early Quaternary periods |
| Grape varieties | Red wine: 49% Merlot, 46% Cabernet Sauvignon, 3% Cabernet franc, 2% Petit Verdot |
| | White wine: 45% Sauvignon, 45% Sémillon, 5% Sauvignon gris, 5% Muscadelle |
| Barrel ageing | Red wine: 18 months - White wine: 12-14 months - New barrels: 70% |
| Second wine | Clémentin |

Manager: Jeanne Lacombe

Château Pape Clément 216 avenue du Docteur Nancel Pénard - 33600 Pessac
GPS: Latitude: 44.80638 - Longitude: - 0.647112
Tel. + 33 (0)5 57 26 38 38 - Fax + 33 (0)5 57 26 38 39
j.lacombe@pape-clement.com - **www.bernard-magrez.com**

# CHÂTEAU PICQUE CAILLOU

| PESSAC-LÉOGNAN | *Owners: Isabelle and Paulin Calvet* |
|---|---|

Built in 1755, Château Picque Caillou is located on the outskirts of the city of Bordeaux, in the historic Pessac-Léognan appellation, the cradle of regional winegrowing.

A close neighbour of the prestigious châteaux Haut-Brion and Pape Clément, Picque Caillou has stony soil deposited by the Garonne River over centuries (as reflected by its name, since caillou means "pebble" in French). Consisting of fine gravel, the well-drained subsoil is responsible for wines of great finesse, elegance, and ageing potential.

In 2007, Paulin Calvet took over management and breathed new life into the estate, which quickly gained recognition from wine professionals, who acknowledged its fine, reliable quality. That same year, consulting oenologists Professor Denis Dubourdieu and Madame Valérie Lavigne began providing technical assistance to the new team. Their combined efforts have resulted in first-class wines of remarkable balance and delicacy that are highly representative of the famous Pessac-Léognan appellation.

| | |
|---|---|
| Area under vine | 22 hectares |
| Production | Red wine: 70,000 bottles - White wine: 8,000 bottles |
| Soil | Gravel |
| Grape varieties | Red wine: 55% Cabernet Sauvignon, 40% Merlot, and 5% Petit Verdot |
| | White wine: 75% Sauvignon Blanc, and 25% Sémillon |
| Barrel ageing | Red wine: 12 months - White wine: 7 months - New barrels: Red wine: 35% - White wine: 20% |
| Second wine | La Réserve de Picque Caillou |

Vineyard Manager: Paulin Calvet - Cellar Master: Amandine Capella

Château Picque Caillou 93 avenue Pierre Mendès France - 33700 Mérignac
GPS: Latitude: 44.823801 - Longitude: -0.63688
Tel. +33 (0)5 56 47 37 98 - Fax +33 (0)5 56 97 99 37
contact@picque-caillou.com - **www.picque-caillou.com**

# CHÂTEAU SMITH HAUT LAFITTE

## CRU CLASSÉ DE GRAVES

**PESSAC-LÉOGNAN**                    *Owners: Florence and Daniel Cathiard*

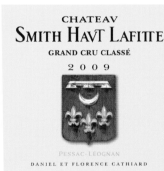

Founded in 1365, this great growth owned by remarkable figures such as the Scottish navigator Georges Smith in the 18th century and Lodi Duffour-Dubergier in the 19th century, owes its reputation as "the quintessential Graves" to its superb terroir of günzian gravel in a single block.

Since its purchase by Florence and Daniel Cathiard in 1990, Smith Haut Lafitte has settled among the leading great growths of Bordeaux thanks to its elegant, complex, powerful and balanced red and white wines, faithful to their terroir.

This internationally recognised level of quality is due to 25 years of "bio precision" work, a unique approach that combines the best of nature and the best of science.

A must for wine lovers visiting the Bordeaux region, Château Smith Haut Lafitte is open seven days a week upon reservation. Come and discover the cooperage, the underground cellar with a thousand barrels, the gravity operated vat room that vinifies "terroir entities" separately, the farm, the "stealth cellar" inspired by the circular economy and see the horses ploughing the vineyard in front of the windows of Les Sources de Caudalie and its famous spa.

| | |
|---|---|
| Area under vine | 78 hectares |
| Production | Red wine: 120,000 bottles - White wine: 38,000 bottles |
| Soil | Günz gravel |
| Grape varieties | Red wine: 60% Cabernet Sauvignon, 30% Merlot, 9% Cabernet franc, 1% Petit Verdot |
| | White wine: 90% Sauvignon blanc, 5% Sauvignon gris, 5% Sémillon |
| Barrel ageing | Red wine: 18 months - White wine: 12 months - New barrels: Red wine: 60% - White wine: 50% |
| Second wine | Les Hauts de Smith - Le Petit Haut Lafitte |

Technical Director: Fabien Teitgen - Commercial Director: Ludovic Fradin – Cellarmaster: Yann Laudeho

Château Smith Haut Lafitte 33650 Martillac
GPS: Latitude: 44.7332 - Longitude: -0.5598
Tel. +33 (0)5 57 83 11 22 - Fax +33 (0)5 57 83 11 21
f.cathiard@smith-haut-lafitte.com - **www.smith-haut-lafitte.com**

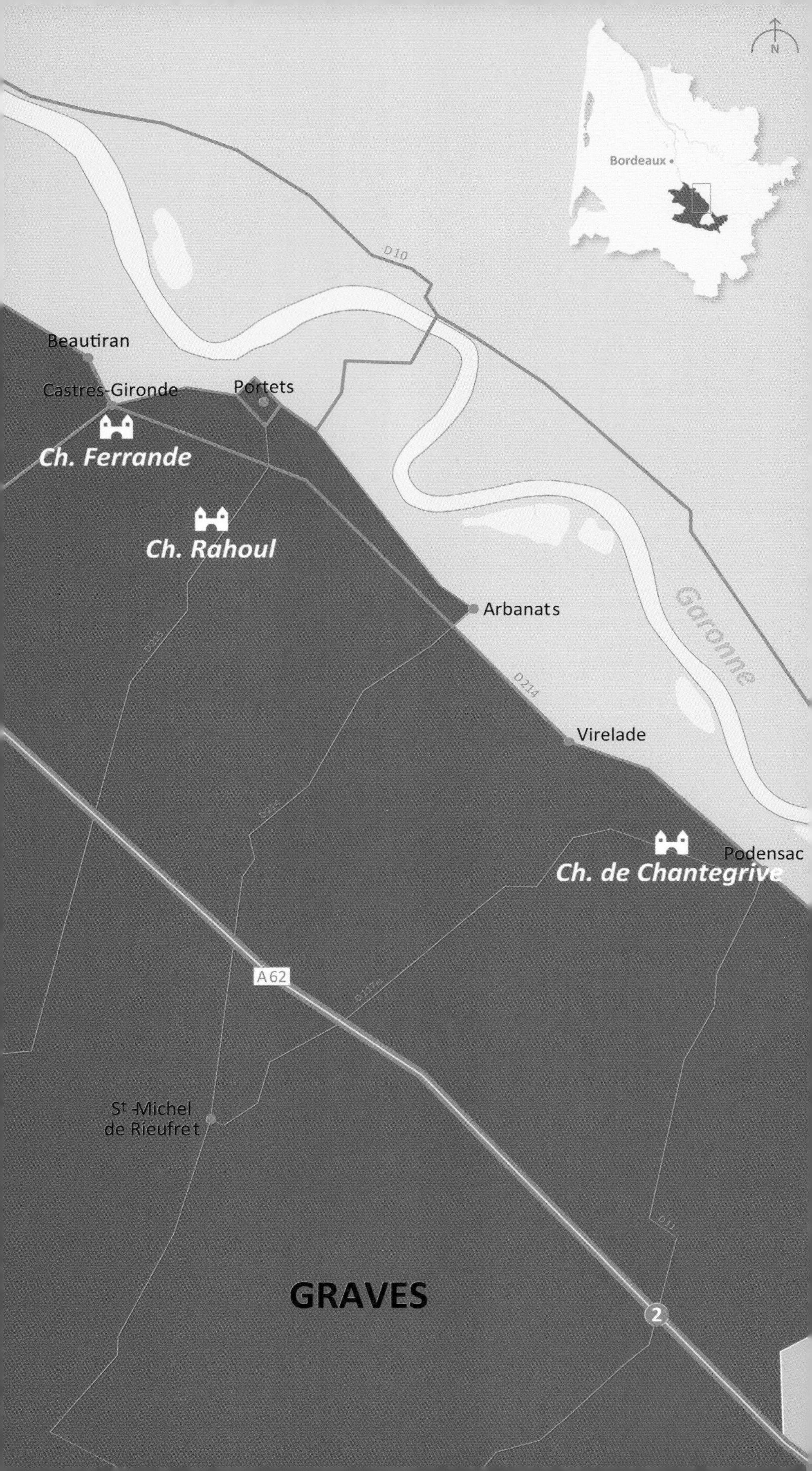

N

Bordeaux

Beautiran

Castres-Gironde        Portets

*Ch. Ferrande*

*Ch. Rahoul*

Arbanats

Virelade

Garonne

D 10

D 215

D 214

*Ch. de Chantegrive*

Podensac

A 62

D 1176

St-Michel
de Rieufret

**GRAVES**

2

# CRUS DE GRAVES

The Graves region, stretching south from the city of Bordeaux to Langon and beyond, produces a wide range of excellent wines. The Graves were famous for their dry and semi-sweet white wines, as well as their red wines, as early as the 13th and 14th centuries. These were very popular with the English and Dutch, who spread their reputation worldwide.

The appellation is the only one in the world whose name identifies the nature of its terroir: graves = gravel. The soil is ideal for winegrowing, and virtually unsuited to any other crop.

# CHÂTEAU DE CHANTEGRIVE

**GRAVES**  *Owner: the Lévêque family*

Château de Chantegrive is located in Podensac in a beautiful Italian like setting overlooking acacia trees and vines typical of the Graves appellation.

The south-facing vines are surrounded by a low stone wall and soak up the warm sunlight on beautiful summer days.

There are river stones ranging in colour from pink to beige on the vineyard's fine sandy soil.

In autumn, one can hear the sound of secateurs as well as pickers singing. Grape bunches fill up crates as people tease one another and talk about their lives.

Chantegrive is a dream that knows no frontiers.

Created in 1966 by Henri and Françoise Lévêque thanks to the sale of their precious stamp collection, Chantegrive continues to please customers around the world. The wine is expertly blended, elegant, and refined. It is much appreciated for its reliable quality. In conjunction with the cellar master, consulting oenologist Hubert de Boüard, owner of Château Angélus, ensures that Chantegrive is excellent in all vintages.

| | |
|---|---|
| Area under vine | 91 hectares |
| Production | Red wine: 210,000 bottles - White wine: 60,000 bottles |
| Soil | Coarse gravel with layers of fine or medium-grain sand on a clay-limestone subsoil |
| Grape varieties | Red wine: 50% Merlot, 50% Cabernet Sauvignon |
| | White wine: 50% Sémillon, 50% Sauvignon Blanc |
| Barrel ageing | Red wine: 12 months - White wine: 9 months - New barrels: Red wine: 50% - White wine: 50% |
| Second wine | Benjamin de Chantegrive |

President: Françoise Lévêque - Managing Director: Marie-Hélène Lévêque - Consulting oenologist: Hubert de Boüard

Château de Chantegrive 44, cours Georges Clémenceau - 33720 Podensac
GPS: Latitude: 44.6529498 - Longitude: -0.3593362
Tel. +33 (0)5 56 27 17 38 - Fax. +33 (0)5 56 27 29 42
courrier@chateau-chantegrive.com - **www.chantegrive.com**

# CHÂTEAU FERRANDE

*Owner: Châteaux et Domaines Castel*

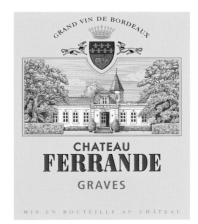

Château Ferrande is located in the commune de Castres-Gironde, in the heart of the Graves. The beautiful manor house, restored in the late 19th century, overlooks a vineyard that is much older.

Ferrande is located near the town of Castres on the Bordeaux-Toulouse road. The known presence of Romans in the commune as early as the 1st century B.C. makes it more than likely that wine was produced here at a very early date. A manor house has existed on the estate since the late 15th century. According to land records, the vineyard has expanded significantly over the centuries.

Rich owners and major négociants succeeded one another at Ferrande. In the 1960s, Admiral Delnaud, a lover of both fine wine and horse racing, purchased the château.

The Castel family acquired Ferrande in 1992. They have made many investments in the vineyard and cellars since then, and Château Ferrande's former lustre is being increasingly restored with each passing year.

| | |
|---|---|
| Area under vine | 98 hectares |
| Production | 450,000 bottles |
| Soil | Gravel |
| Grape varieties | Red wine: 50% Merlot, 50% Cabernet |
| | White wine: 30% Sauvignon blanc, 30% Sauvignon gris, 40% Sémillon |
| Barrel ageing | Red wine: 14 months - White wine: 10 months - New barrels: Red wine: 30% - White wine: 15% |

Public Relations for Châteaux et Domaines Castel: Véréna Raoux

Château Ferrande Route du bois de Savi - 33640 Castres
GPS: Latitude: 44.694538 - Longitude: -0.442726
Tel. +33 (0)5 56 35 72 73
contact@chateaux-castel.com - **www.chateau-ferrande.com**

# CHÂTEAU RAHOUL

*Owner: Alain Thiénot*

Grand vin de Bordeaux
1646
CHATEAU RAHOUL
GRAVES

VIGNOBLES DOURTHE

In 1646, Chevalier Guillaume Rahoul built a lovely manor house which he named after himself. The vineyards were expanded in the late 18th century by Pierre Balguerie, at which time Rahoul grew to its present boundaries.

Thanks to English, Australian, and Danish owners, Château Rahoul attained international recognition starting in the 1970s. Alain Thiénot, from Champagne, who already possessed vineyards in Bordeaux, bought Rahoul in 1986 and undertook an ambitious modernisation programme. The acquisition of a shareholding by Dourthe in the Thienot group in 2007 was a benchmark in the château's uncompromising approach to quality. Sizeable investments were made in renovating the vineyard and equipping the cellars, and the wine is now made by the Dourthe team, relying of state-of-the-art techniques.

Unusual in that it is made predominantly from Sémillon, the white wine faithfully reflects the finesse and elegance of Rahoul's terroir. The attractive red wine features a very refined style, silky tannin, and a full, rich flavour.

| Area under vine | 39.4 hectares |
| --- | --- |
| Production | Red wine: 100,000 bottles - White wine: 12,000 bottles |
| Soil | Sandy-gravel and clay-gravel |
| Grape varieties | Red wine: 67% Merlot, 30% Cabernet Sauvignon, 3% Petit Verdot |
| | White wine: 65% Sémillon, 35% Sauvignon Blanc |
| Barrel ageing | Red wine: 12-14 months - White wine: 8-10 months |
| | New barrels: Red wine: 20-30% - White wine: 10-20% |
| Second wine | L'Orangerie de Rahoul |

Manager: Vignobles Dourthe - President: Patrick Jestin - Director: Frédéric Bonnaffous

Château Rahoul 4 route du Courneau - 33640 Portets
GPS: Latitude: 44.687950 - Longitude: -0.425884
Tel. +33 (0)5 56 35 53 00 - Fax +33 (0)5 56 35 53 29
contact@dourthe.com - **www.chateau-rahoul.com**

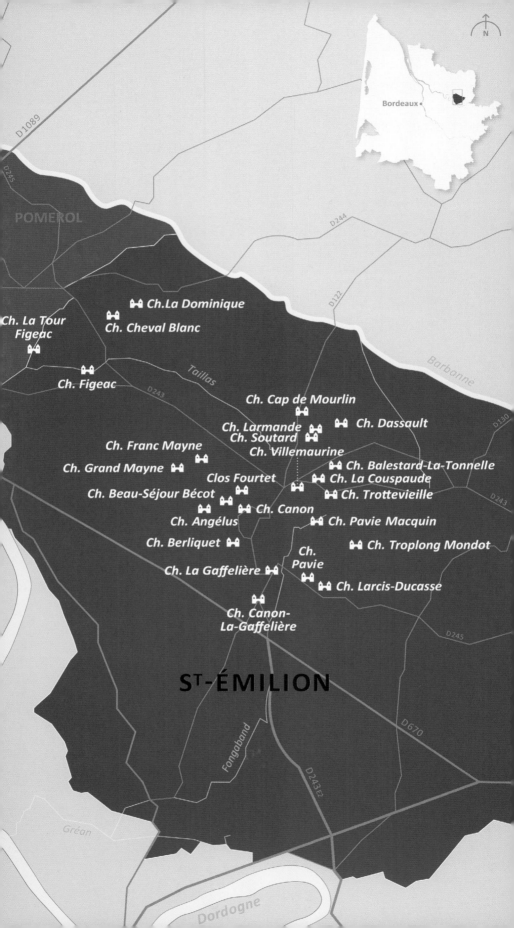

N

Bordeaux

D1089

D245

POMEROL

D244

D122

Barbonne

D130

Ch.La Dominique

Ch. La Tour
Figeac

Ch. Cheval Blanc

Taillas

Ch. Figeac

D243

Ch. Cap de Mourlin

Ch. Larmande

Ch. Dassault

Ch. Soutard

Ch. Franc Mayne

Ch. Villemaurine

Ch. Grand Mayne

Ch. Balestard-La-Tonnelle

Clos Fourtet

Ch. La Couspaude

Ch. Beau-Séjour Bécot

Ch. Trottevieille

Ch. Canon

Ch. Angélus

Ch. Pavie Macquin

Ch. Berliquet

Ch. Troplong Mondot

Ch. La Gaffelière

Ch.
Pavie

Ch. Larcis-Ducasse

Ch. Canon-
La-Gaffelière

D245

St-ÉMILION

Fongaband

D243 E2

D670

Gréan

Dordogne

# CRUS DE SAINT-ÉMILION

Edward I, King of England, delimited the Jurisdiction of Saint-Émilion, consisting of nine parishes, in 1289. Since then, only wines produced in one of these communes is entitled to the Saint-Émilion appellation. Saint-Émilion's superb reputation is due primarily to wines from the côtes, plateau, and graves areas.

The picturesque medieval village of Saint-Émilion is an architectural jewel, built in a half circle on hills opposite the Dordogne. The steep, narrow streets, Romanesque and Gothic churches, monasteries, and cloisters make this one of the loveliest villages in France. Listed as a World Heritage Site by UNESCO, Saint-Émilion is an outstanding location which the members of the Union des Grands Crus will be delighted to help you discover.

# CHÂTEAU ANGÉLUS
## PREMIER GRAND CRU CLASSÉ "A"

## SAINT-ÉMILION GRAND CRU

Located less than a kilometre from the steeple of the church in Saint-Émilion, on the famous pied de côte (or "foot of the slope") with south-facing sun exposure, Château Angélus reflects the winemaking passion of eight generations of the de Boüard de Laforest family.

The château name comes from the fact that sounds are amplified in this vineyard located in the heart of a natural amphitheatre. Workers could therefore heard the angelus, or call to prayer, ringing simultaneously from three local churches. Over the centuries, the angelus has rung out morning, noon, and night, summoning men and women in the vines and the village to stop working in order to pray. The bell on Château Angélus's label and bottle symbolises the origin of the name and these moments of contemplation.

Recognized around the world as one of the jewels of Saint-Émilion, Château Angélus' success is due to the dedication of a family and a winemaking team devoted to their terroir and faithful to very high standards. Work in both the vineyard and

| | |
|---|---|
| Area under vine | 39 hectares |
| Production | 100,000 bottles |
| Soil | Clay-limestone on the upper part and clay-sand-limestone on the hillside |
| Grape varieties | 50% Merlot, 47% Cabernet Franc, and 3% Cabernet Sauvignon |
| Barrel ageing | 18-24 months - New barrels: 100 % |
| Second wine | Le Carillon d'Angélus |

Managers: Hubert de Boüard de Laforest - Jean-Bernard Grenié - Stéphanie de Boüard- Rivoal

Château Angélus 33330 Saint-Émilion
GPS: Latitude: 44.8928817 - Longitude: -0.1704865
Tel. +33 (0)5 57 24 71 39 - Fax +33 (0)5 57 24 68 56
angelus@angelus.com - **www.angelus.com**

the cellar is done with great respect for tradition, but also taking advantage of state-of-the-art techniques to make most of each vintage.

Angélus is marked by an audacious choice of grape varieties to match an outstanding terroir. Its unique character - combining richness, concentration, elegance, and purity - is due to the high percentage of Cabernet Franc grown on Saint-Émilion's southern slope.

# CHÂTEAU PAVIE
## PREMIER GRAND CRU CLASSÉ "A"

## SAINT-ÉMILION GRAND CRU

Château Pavie's history goes back to Roman times. The first vines in Saint-Emilion were planted on the slopes of Ausone and Pavie in the 4th century AD. At the time, the limestone plateau was devoted to mixed farming.

Up until the 18th century, "pavies" or clingstone vineyard peaches with red flesh were grown here. Over the years, the peach trees gradually disappeared, and were replaced by vines.

The outstanding quality of the terroir on the famous south-facing Côte de Pavie was revealed over generations, and became widely-acknowledged by the mid-twentieth century.

Impressed by the estate's history, geographical location, and terroir, Gérard Perse acquired Château Pavie in 1998.

He is responsible for the château's renaissance. Nothing deterred him from his goal of making Château Pavie one of the very best wines in the appellation.

Gérard Perse now shares this passion for viticulture and winemaking with his daughter, Angélique, and her husband, Henrique Da Costa, both of whom are involved in managing the estate.

Château Pavie has 37 hectares of vines in a single block with three different terroirs: clay-limestone plateau, clay slope, and gravel and clay soil at the foot of the slope.

| | |
|---|---|
| Area under vine | 37 hectares |
| Production | 80,000 bottles |
| Soil | Limestone plateau, clay-limestone on the middle of the slope, and gravel at the bottom of the slope |
| Grape varieties | 60 % Merlot, 25 % Cabernet Franc, and 15 % Cabernet Sauvignon |
| Barrel ageing | 24 months - New barrels: 70-100% |
| Second wine | Arômes de Pavie |

Château Pavie 2, Pimpinelle - 33330 Saint-Émilion
GPS: Latitude: 44.883204 - Longitude: -0.151309
Tel. +33(0)5 57 55 43 43 - Fax +33 (0)5 57 24 63 99
contact@vignoblesperse.com - **www.vignoblesperse.com**

The blend of wine from these different terroirs, combined with low yields and the separate fermentation of grapes from each individual plot in temperature-controlled oak vats, produces a wine of unique complexity. Displaying marvellous structure and elegance, Château Pavie is made in magnificent facilities designed by the famous architect and decorator Alberto Pinto.

On the 6th of September 2012, Château Pavie was promoted to Premier Grand Cru Classé "A" status, joining the closed circle of the ten greatest estates in Bordeaux.

This was the ultimate recognition of the efforts made by Gérard Perse and his team over the years in the vineyard and cellars.

# CHÂTEAU BALESTARD LA TONNELLE

## GRAND CRU CLASSÉ

## SAINT-ÉMILION GRAND CRU
*Owner: Jacques Capdemourlin*

The name of this estate with 10.6 hectares of vines has two different origins. "Balestard" was a former canon of the Chapter of Saint-Émilion, and "La Tonnelle" refers to the 15th-century stone watchtower that still stands in the heart of the vineyard.

The château's reputation dates back to François Villon who cited it in a poem that is reproduced on the label of the grand vin.

Located a stone's throw from the medieval town of Saint-Émilion, atop a slope on a clay-limestone plateau, the charming vineyard has a superb terroir. The present owner, Jacques Capdemourlin, manages the estate with the greatest care and attention.

The wine is fermented the traditional way and then aged in oak barrels, half of which are new every year. Combining respect for the terroir, tradition, and the best modern techniques, Balestard La Tonnelle produces full-bodied wine of extreme elegance, one of the finest grands crus classés in Saint-Émilion.

48

| Area under vine | 10.6 hectares |
|---|---|
| Production | 55,000 bottles |
| Soil | Clay-limestone plateau |
| Grape varieties | 70% Merlot, 25% Cabernet franc, 5% Cabernet Sauvignon |
| Barrel ageing | 15-18 months - New barrels: 50% |
| Second wine | Chanoine de Balestard |

Château Balestard La Tonnelle 33330 Saint-Émilion
GPS: Latitude: 44.89953 - Longitude: -0.14621
Tel. +33 (0)5 57 74 62 06 - Fax +33 (0)5 57 74 59 34
info@vignoblescapdemourlin.com - **www.vignoblescapdemourlin.com**

# CHÂTEAU BEAU-SÉJOUR BÉCOT
## PREMIER GRAND CRU CLASSÉ

## SAINT-ÉMILION GRAND CRU  Owners: Gérard, Dominique and Juliette Bécot

Located immediately west of the magical town of Saint-Émilion on the Saint-Martin de Mazerat limestone plateau, Beau-Séjour Bécot is in the heart of the appellation. The estate has been devoted to winemaking since the Gallo-Roman period. In 1787, General Jacques de Carles, wishing to commemorate for all time the pleasure that he enjoyed staying there, named the estate "Beau-Séjour" (meaning "lovely stay").

In 1969, Michel Bécot acquired the château and brought the area under vine up to 18.50 hectares thanks to the purchase of neighbouring vineyard plots with the same terroir. He also turned seven hectares of former underground limestone quarries into a storage cellar where tens of thousands of bottles age under ideal conditions. His work in improving and embellishing the estate went on until his retirement in 1985.

His two sons, Gérard and Dominique, have followed in their father's footsteps while introducing numerous technical innovations to both the cellars and the vineyard. Only the ripest, healthiest grapes are now harvested, and then sorted one by one. Gérard's daughter, Juliette, started working at the château in 2001 in order to market wines from the family estate.

| | |
|---|---|
| Area under vine | 19.04 hectares |
| Production | 60,000 bottles |
| Soil | clay and asteriated limestone |
| Grape varieties | 70% Merlot, 24% Cabernet franc, 6% Cabernet Sauvignon |
| Barrel ageing | 16-18 months - New barrels: 70-80% |
| Second wine | Tournelle de Beau-Séjour Bécot |

Co-managers: Gérard Bécot - Dominique Bécot - Juliette Bécot

Château Beau-Séjour Bécot 1 La Carte – 33330 Saint-Émilion
GPS: Latitude: 44.896063 - Longitude: -0.163236
Tel. +33 (0)5 57 74 46 87 - Fax +33 (0)5 57 24 66 88
contact@beausejour-becot.com - **www.beausejour-becot.com**

# CHÂTEAU BERLIQUET
## GRAND CRU CLASSÉ

## SAINT-ÉMILION GRAND CRU — *Owner: Viscount Patrick de Lesquen*

Berliquet is one of the oldest vineyards in Saint-Émilion and appears on Belleyme's map dating back to 1768. In his 1828 classification, Paguierre lists Berliquet as one of the appellation's five first growths. Belonging to the de Sèze, and then the Pérès families, it was acquired in 1918 by Count de Carles, the current owner's grandfather. Château Berliquet was accorded its rightful place among the greatest wines of Saint-Émilion in the 1986 classification.

The estate is located on the Magdelaine plateau, a few hundred metres from the town of Saint-Émilion. The vines have south and southwest-facing sun exposure and border on several Premiers Grands Crus Classés. The wine is aged in magnificent underground cellars hewn out of solid rock.

The arrival of Nicolas Thienpont and Stéphane Derenoncourt in July 2008 made it possible to define the needs of each vineyard plot and achieve optimum ripeness to reflect the full elegance of the terroir.

50

| | |
|---|---|
| Area under vine | 9 hectares |
| Production | 30,000 bottles |
| Soil | Limestone and clay-limestone |
| Grape varieties | 70% Merlot, 25% Cabernet franc, 5% Cabernet Sauvignon |
| Barrel ageing | 12-16 months - New barrels: 50% |
| Second wine | Les Ailes de Berliquet |

Manager: Nicolas Thienpont - Consultant: Stéphane Derenoncourt - Co-Manager: Jérôme de Lesquen

Château Berliquet 33330 Saint-Émilion
GPS: Latitude: 44.8894515 - Longitude: -0.1650495
Tel. +33 (0)5 57 24 70 48 - Fax +33 (0)5 57 24 70 24
chateau.berliquet@wanadoo.fr

# CHÂTEAU CANON
## PREMIER GRAND CRU CLASSÉ

## SAINT-ÉMILION GRAND CRU

*Owner: Chanel*

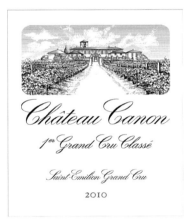

Located on the Saint-Émilion limestone plateau, Château Canon is an emblematic estate with an outstanding terroir entitling it to Premier Grand Cru Classé status since 1954.

The château overlooks a gentle slope where vines have been grown for a millennium. This vineyard is surrounded by stone walls and stretches as far as the village of Saint-Émilion

The enthusiastic winemaking team does their utmost to reflect Canon's superb terroir by producing wine with unique finesse and complexity.

Like the maison Chanel, who have owned Canon since 1996, Château Canon epitomises a style that is timeless, elegant and always fashionable.

| | |
|---|---|
| Area under vine | 32 hectares |
| Production | 85,000 bottles |
| Soil | Asteriated limestone plateau with clay veins |
| Grape varieties | 70% Merlot, 30% Cabernet franc |
| Barrel ageing | 18 months - New barrels: 70% |
| Second wine | Clos Canon |

Managing Director: Nicolas Audebert

Château Canon BP22 - 33330 Saint-Émilion
GPS: Latitude: 44.893701 - Longitude: -0.162392
Tel. +33 (0)5 57 55 23 45 - Fax +33 (0)5 57 24 68 00
contact@chateau-canon.com - **www.chateaucanon.com**

# CHÂTEAU CANON-LA-GAFFELIÈRE

## PREMIER GRAND CRU CLASSÉ

## SAINT-ÉMILION GRAND CRU

*Owners: Counts von Neipperg*

Located on the slope and the foot of the slope south of the medieval village of Saint-Émilion, Château Canon-La-Gaffelière has belonged to the Counts von Neipperg since 1971. The terroir consists of clay-limestone and clay-sand soil that is particularly efficient at capturing and retaining heat. The choice of grape varieties is rather atypical for the appellation in light of the soil: almost a perfect 50/50 divide between Merlot and Cabernet.

Certified for organic viticulture since the 2014 vintage, the estate produces elegant wines year in and year out. Remarkably well-structured and complex, Canon-La-Gaffelière is pure and unfailingly elegant, reflecting the uncompromising way in which it is made.

Representing some eight centuries of family winegrowing tradition, Count Stephan von Neipperg has succeeded in promoting Château Canon-La-Gaffelière to Premier Grand Cru Classé de Saint-Émilion status thanks to a winegrowing philosophy that gives priority not only to quality, but also respect for an outstanding terroir.

| | |
|---|---|
| Area under vine | 19.5 hectares |
| Production | 65,000 bottles |
| Soil | Clay-limestone and clay-sand soil at the foot of the slope |
| Grape varieties | 55% Merlot, 40% Cabernet franc, 5% Cabernet Sauvignon |
| Barrel ageing | 15-20 months - New barrels: 80-100% |
| Second wine | Les Hauts de Canon La Gaffelière |

Manager: Count Stephan von Neipperg

Château Canon-La-Gaffelière 33330 Saint-Émilion
GPS: Latitude: 44.881228 - Longitude: -0.160501
Tel. +33 (0)5 57 24 71 33 - Fax +33 (0)5 57 24 67 95
info@neipperg.com - **www.neipperg.com**

# CHÂTEAU CAP DE MOURLIN
## GRAND CRU CLASSÉ

The Capdemourlin family has owned vineyards in Saint-Émilion for nearly four centuries, as attested by a wine sales contract dating from 1647. In an unusual departure from practices at the time, this document mentions the place name of the vineyard and the name of the wine, one of the oldest in Saint-Émilion.

In 1983, Jacques Capdemourlin, the present owner, reunited this estate that had been divided between his father and his uncle for many years. He also undertook a major renovation in order to introduce modern fermentation and ageing techniques (a new vat room, new air-conditioned area for malolactic fermentation, and new barrel ageing cellar).

The 14-hectare vineyard is ideally situated on slopes north of the town of Saint-Émilion with clay-limestone and clay-siliceous soil. Château Cap de Mourlin's wine is both generous and extremely elegant, with a very expressive bouquet. It is one of the most highly-reputed wines of Saint-Émilion.

| | |
|---|---|
| Area under vine | 14 hectares |
| Production | 70,000 bottles |
| Soil | Clay-limestone and clay-siliceous |
| Grape varieties | 65% Merlot, 25% Cabernet franc, 10% Cabernet Sauvignon |
| Barrel ageing | 15-18 months - New barrels: 50% |
| Second wine | Capitan de Mourlin |

Château Cap de Mourlin 33330 Saint-Émilion
GPS: Latitude: 44.9076845 - Longitude: -0.1540661
Tel. +33 (0)5 57 74 62 06 - Fax +33 (0)5 57 74 59 34
info@vignoblescapdemourlin.com - **www.vignoblescapdemourlin.com**

53

# CHÂTEAU LA COUSPAUDE
## GRAND CRU CLASSÉ

## SAINT-ÉMILION GRAND CRU
*Owner: the Aubert family*

Château La Couspaude is located in the heart of Saint-Émilion, near the famous monolithic church carved out of solid rock. La Couspaude has been the pride and joy of the Aubert family (who also own other estates in the region) for over a century. In fact, the Auberts have been making fine wine in Bordeaux for over two centuries and have unquestionably maintained the family tradition of quality and respect for the terroir to the present day.

La Couspaude, was called "La Croix Paute" in the Middle Ages in reference to the cross that still marks the intersection of two roads in front of the estate, and which served as a meeting point for pilgrims on their way to Santiago de Compostela.

This magnificent estate is on the Saint-Émilion limestone plateau, entirely surrounded by walls like all the village's most ancient vineyards. Château La Couspaude also has underground cellars where the wine is fermented and aged in barrels, as well as an impressive reception room that serves as venue for important functions.

| | |
|---|---|
| Area under vine | 7 hectares |
| Production | 36,000 bottles |
| Soil | Clay-limestone plateau with a limestone and asteriated subsoil |
| Grape varieties | 75% Merlot, 20% Cabernet Sauvignon, 5% Cabernet franc |
| Barrel ageing | 16-20 months - New barrels: 80-100% |
| Second wine | Junior de la Couspaude |

Château la Couspaude BP 40 - 33330 Saint-Émilion
GPS: Latitude: 44.896979 - Longitude: -0.1490804
Tel. +33 (0)5 57 40 15 76 - Fax +33 (0)5 57 40 10 14
vignobles.aubert@wanadoo.fr - **www.aubert-vignobles.com**

# CHÂTEAU DASSAULT
## GRAND CRU CLASSÉ

## SAINT-ÉMILION GRAND CRU
*Owner: Dassault Wine Estates*

The Dassault family, passionate pioneers in the aeronautic industry, new technologies and the art market, became interested in fine wines very early.

Marcel Dassault was a visionary business leader. He bought Château Couperie in 1955 on an impulse. He gave his family name to the property and put everything in place to make it a famous classified growth. The property has seen the quality of its wines improve vintage after vintage.

In 1969, with its promotion to the rank of Grand Cru Classé, Château Dassault achieved the status it deserved.

The entire purpose and mission of Dassault Wine Estates is to pass on, over time, the necessary conditions for the crafting of fine wines. The Dassault family created Dassaut Wine Estates because quality wine has today become a major issue on a global dimension.

It is a way of life, a heritage, a sign of excellence. It has become essential to apply these same values to the wine sector and contribute to the longevity of french know-how and expertise.

These entrepreneurial values of passion, progress and a permanent search for excellence, the values of the Dassault family, apply to all the group's wine-related activities.

Over the years, the properties owned by Dassault Wine Estates have increased to nearly fifty hectares and now form one of the largest vineyard holdings in Saint-Emilion.

| | |
|---|---|
| Area under vine | 24 hectares |
| Production | 90,000 bottles |
| Soil | Sand and siliceous-limestone soil |
| Grape varieties | 75% Merlot, 20% Cabernet franc, 5% Cabernet Sauvignon |
| Barrel ageing | 14-18 months - New barrels: 75%-85% |
| Second wine | D de Dassault |

President: Laurent Dassault - Managing Director: Laurence Brun

Château Dassault BP 35 - 33330 Saint-Émilion
GPS: Latitude: 44.894387 - Longitude: -0.155729
Tel. +33 (0)5 57 55 10 00 - Fax +33 (0)5 57 55 10 01
lbv@dassaultwineestates.com - **www.dassaultwineestates.com**

# CHÂTEAU LA DOMINIQUE
## GRAND CRU CLASSÉ

## SAINT-ÉMILION GRAND CRU

*Owner: Clément Fayat*

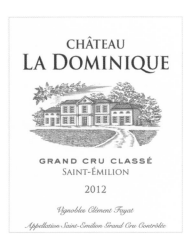

A winegrowing estate since the 16th century, Château La Dominique is ideally situated in the northwest part of the Saint-Emilion appellation. Acquired in 1969 by Clément Fayat, the vineyard has been entirely renovated and constantly improved ever since.

Bordering directly on châteaux Cheval Blanc, Figeac, L'Évangile and La Conseillante, this outstanding 30-hectare terroir consists of sand and clay where Merlot, Cabernet Franc and Cabernet Sauvignon reach full maturity to make great wine.

The vines are tended with meticulous care, and great attention is paid to winemaking and blending with help from the famous consultant Michel Rolland to produce deeply-coloured, generous, intense, opulent and silky wines in every vintage. In keeping with La Dominique's prestigious reputation, an innovative new cellar, both in terms of architecture and technical capabilities, was inaugurated in 2014. Designed by Jean Nouvel, this new building houses both a wine cellar and visitor reception area, and affords a magnificent view of the surrounding vineyards!

56

| | |
|---|---|
| Area under vine | 29 hectares |
| Production | 80,000 bottles |
| Soil | Ancient sand on clay and brown clay soil |
| Grape varieties | 81% Merlot, 16% Cabernet franc, 3% Cabernet Sauvignon |
| Barrel ageing | 16-18 months - New barrels: 70% |
| Second wine | Relais de La Dominique |

Château La Dominique Lieu-dit La Dominique - 33330 Saint-Émilion
GPS: Latitude: 44.920525 - Longitude: -0.186274
Tel. +33 (0)5 57 51 31 36 - Fax +33 (0)5 57 51 63 04
contact@vignobles.fayat.com - **www.vignobles-fayat.com**

# CHÂTEAU-FIGEAC
## PREMIER GRAND CRU CLASSÉ

## SAINT-ÉMILION GRAND CRU
*Owner: the Manoncourt family*

A Saint-Émilion Premier Grand Cru Classé, Château Figeac has belonged to the Manoncourt family for over 120 years. This estate, one of the most prestigious in Bordeaux, includes a 18th century château, 14 hectares of grounds and 40 hectares of vines in a single block. Figeac as we know it today was shaped by several pioneers, such as Thierry Manoncourt, who succeed in creating the wine's unique style.

The château's reputation is due to its fabulous terroir, consisting of three gravelly rises that account for the highest proportion of Cabernet on the Right Bank. Each vintage is made with the greatest of care in the vineyard and the cellar.

Château Figeac produces truly great, elegant wines with a unique character and remarkably reliable quality. They also age outstandingly well.

| | |
|---|---|
| Area under vine | 40 hectares |
| Production | 100,000 bottles |
| Soil | Three gravelly rises |
| Grape varieties | 35% Cabernet Sauvignon, 35% Cabernet franc, 30% Merlot |
| Barrel ageing | 18 months - New barrels: 100% |
| Second wine | Petit-Figeac |

Château de Figeac 33330 Saint-Émilion
GPS: Latitude: 44.912855 - Longitude: -0.19314
Tel. +33 (0)5 57 24 72 26 - Fax +33 (0)5 57 74 45 74
chateau-figeac@chateau-figeac.com - **www.chateau-figeac.com**

# CLOS FOURTET
## PREMIER GRAND CRU CLASSÉ

## SAINT-ÉMILION GRAND CRU

*Owner: Cuvelier Family*

Clos Fourtet owes its initial reputation to the Rulleau and Carles families, Lords of Figeac. In the 18th century, they were the first to make the most of this land with only a thin layer of arable soil, but blessed with outstanding natural drainage. Clos Fourtet has abundantly proved its standing as a Premier Grand Cru Classé, helped in this respect by hard work and major investments by the Cuvelier family, owners since 2001.

Located atop the limestone plateau well-known for producing some of the greatest wines in Saint-Émilion, Clos Fourtet has one of the appellation's best and most famous terroirs.

The vines, located in a single block, a stone'st throw from the medieval village, grow atop impressive underground quarries.

Winemaking is very traditional, but complemented by the most up-to-date techniques. The wine is extremely elegant and has a strong personality, with incomparable minerality and freshness.

58

| | |
|---|---|
| Area under vine | 18.5 hectares |
| Production | 55,000 bottles |
| Soil | Clay-limestone plateau |
| Grape varieties | 85% Merlot, 10% Cabernet Sauvignon, 5% Cabernet franc |
| Barrel ageing | 15-18 months - New barrels: 65% |
| Second wine | Closerie de Fourtet |

Manager: Matthieu Cuvelier - Director: Tony Ballu

Clos de Fourtet 1 Châtelet Sud - 33330 Saint-Émilion
GPS: Latitude: 44.8953455 - Longitude: -0.1634372
Tel. +33 (0)5 57 24 70 90 - Fax +33 (0)5 57 74 46 52
closfourtet@closfourtet.com - **www.closfourtet.com**

# CHÂTEAU FRANC MAYNE
## GRAND CRU CLASSÉ

## SAINT-ÉMILION GRAND CRU
*Owners: Griet Van Malderen-Laviale and Hervé Laviale*

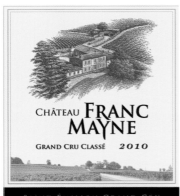

One reaches Château Franc Mayne by going along a long drive with Merlot vines on either side. Located on the Côte de Franc, which gave its name to the estate, part of the vineyard is steep and part is on the limestone plateau. The topsoil consists of a thin layer of clay with limestone outcrops. Traces of an ancient Gallo-Roman road run alongside the property and a former coaching inn bears witness to the steady flow of pilgrims on their way to Santiago de Compostela.

The owners felt that the grapes needed a worthy architectural and technological showcase so they built a new vat room (with small stainless steel and oak vats to ferment fruit from each plot separately) as well as a new first year cellar in 2005. The wines finish ageing in former underground quarries. These magical cellars, spread out over more than two hectares, are visited by thousands of wine enthusiasts every year.

The château also features a 12-room boutique hotel and a natural swimming pool. Franc Mayne epitomises everything that has made Saint-Émilion world-famous!

| | |
|---|---|
| Area under vine | 7 hectares |
| Production | 28,000 bottles |
| Soil | Clay-limestone on the plateau and slope, clay-sand at the foot of the slope |
| Grape varieties | 90% Merlot, 10% Cabernet franc |
| Barrel ageing | 18 months - New barrels: 60-80% |
| Second wine | Les Cèdres de Franc Mayne |

Château Franc Mayne 14 La Gomerie (RD243) - 33330 Saint-Émilion
GPS: Latitude: 44.90277 - Longitude: -0.16896
Tel. +33 (0)5 57 24 62 61 - Fax +33 (0)5 57 24 68 25
info@chateaufrancmayne.com - **www.chateaufrancmayne.com**

# CHÂTEAU LA GAFFELIÈRE

## PREMIER GRAND CRU CLASSÉ

## SAINT-ÉMILION GRAND CRU — *Owner: Count Léo de Malet Roquefort*

Vines have been grown at Château La Gaffelière since the Gallo-Roman period, as proved by the numerous mosaics discovered by Count Léo de Malet Roquefort in 1969. Perhaps it is just a coincidence, but the poet Ausone is known to have had a vineyard in this area at about the same time the villa was built, in the 4th century AD. It is thus very likely that the mosaics decorated the rooms of his villa. The quality of these mosaics show that the owner was clearly prosperous. The location is still called Le Palat, meaning "the Palace".

The unbroken presence of the de Malet Roquefort family at La Gaffelière for over three centuries makes them the oldest winegrowing family in Saint-Emilion. This gives the estate a special aura and legitimacy.

Today, father and son work together to make the most of this unique vineyard with the same passion as their ancestors, combining time-honoured traditions and modern techniques in an on-going quest for perfection. They are helped in this by a dynamic and professional winemaking team.

Château La Gaffelière is one of the jewels of the Saint-Émilion appellation, and places great emphasis on quality, tradition and terroir. The wine is famous for its complexity, elegance and subtle finesse, as well as its ability to age well for decades.

| | |
|---|---|
| Area under vine | 19 hectares |
| Production | 60,000 bottles |
| Soil | Clay-limestone |
| Grape varieties | 70% Merlot, 30% Cabernet franc |
| Barrel ageing | 12-14 months - New barrels: 50% |
| Second wine | Clos La Gaffelière |

President: Alexandre de Malet Roquefort

Château La Gaffelière BP 65 - 33330 Saint-Émilion
GPS: Latitude: 44.883364 - Longitude: -0.159473
Tel. +33 (0)5 57 24 72 15 - Fax +33 (0)5 57 24 69 06
contact@gaffeliere.com

# CHÂTEAU GRAND MAYNE
## GRAND CRU CLASSÉ

In keeping with the facade of its 16th century château, Grand Mayne exemplifies the values of authenticity and classic simplicity.

When owned by the Laveau family in the 18th century, the estate cultivated over 100 hectares of various crops. Grand Mayne currently has just 17 hectares of vines, which have become the heart and soul of the estate.

Growing in every direction around the château, which seems to sit on a bed of green, over 100,000 vines cover the gentle slope with southwest sun exposure that catches the last of the setting sun's rays.

Grand Mayne is an authentic, but also a romantic place, where wine is made with an obsession for perfection and adapted to the complex terroir. There is no need to spell out the techniques – it is sufficient to taste the wine to imagine them...

The Nony family has presided over Grand Mayne's destinies since 1934. Jean-Antoine represents the third generation – after Jean, then Jean-Pierre and his wife Marie-Françoise – to perpetuate family management, resolutely turned towards excellence.

| | |
|---|---|
| Area under vine | 17 hectares |
| Production | 55,000 bottles |
| Soil | Clay-limesone soil on the slope, and clay and sand-clay soil at the foot of the slope |
| Grape varieties | 75% Merlot, 20% Cabernet franc, 5% Cabernet Sauvignon |
| Barrel ageing | 18 months - New barrels: 70-80% |
| Second wine | Filia de Grand Mayne |

Manager: Jean-Antoine Nony - Director: Jean-François Plumas - Technical Manager: Marc François

Château Grand Mayne BP 64 - 33330 Saint-Émilion
GPS: Latitude: 44.899538 - Longitude: -0.175223
Tel. +33 (0)5 57 74 42 50 - Fax +33 (0)5 57 74 41 89
contact@grand-mayne.com - **www.grand-mayne.com**

# CHÂTEAU LARCIS DUCASSE
## PREMIER GRAND CRU CLASSÉ

**SAINT-ÉMILION GRAND CRU**　　　*Owner: the Gratiot-Attmane family*

Château Larcis Ducasse, promoted to a Saint-Émilion Premier Grand Cru Classé status in 2012, has belonged to the Gratiot-Attmane family since 1893. Starting in 2002, Nicolas Thienpont and David Suire have perpetuated the family's efforts to produce quality wines, assisted by consultants Stéphane Derenoncourt and Julien Lavenu.

Larcis Ducasse's character is defined by its clay-limestone soil and south-facing sun-exposed slopes conducive to beautiful ripeness. The wines have a fresh, mineral flavour. Their complexity and structure are due to the varied nature of the parent rock, which goes from asteriated limestone on the plateau to feldspathic, iron-rich sandy soil at the foot of the slope.

Merlot and Cabernet Franc vines are planted according to the profile of each part of the vineyard. Work in the vineyard is done meticulously. Fermentation takes place gently and then the wine is aged in barrel for a duration adapted to each vintage. The final blend from this superb terroir results in delicious, elegant and magnificently balanced wines.

62

| | |
|---|---|
| Area under vine | 11 hectares |
| Production | 30,000 bottles |
| Soil | Clay-limestone fossiliferous soil on the southern slope |
| Grape varieties | 78% Merlot, 22% Cabernet franc |
| Barrel ageing | 16 months - New barrels: 65% |
| Second wine | Murmure de Larcis Ducasse |

Estate Manager: Nicolas Thienpont - Technical Director/oenologist: David Suire – Communication: Blandine Giambiasi

Château Larcis Ducasse 33330 Saint-Laurent-des-Combes
GPS: Latitude: 44.880665 - Longitude: -0.145826
Tel. +33 (0)5 57 24 70 84 - Fax +33 (0)5 57 24 64 00
contact@larcis-ducasse.com - **www.larcis-ducasse.com**

# CHÂTEAU LARMANDE
## GRAND CRU CLASSÉ

## SAINT-ÉMILION GRAND CRU

*Owner: Groupe AG2R LA MONDIALE*

Grand Cru Classé

✤

CHATEAU LARMANDE

Saint-Emilion Grand Cru

2012

Château Larmande is one of the oldest estates in the appellation, and local archives contain references going as far back as 1585. It is said that the jurats, or town aldermen, met there. Today, the estate covers 20 hectares, making it one of the largest grands crus classés in Saint-Emilion.

The right balance...

Combining traditional and state-of-the-art winegrowing methods, Larmande has found just the right balance to make superb wine in every vintage. The estate is located just 1,200 metres from the village of Saint-Emilion!

| | |
|---|---|
| Area under vine | 20 hectares |
| Production | 70,000 bottles |
| Soil | Clay-limestone, clay-siliceous, and sand |
| Grape varieties | 65% Merlot, 30% Cabernet franc, 5% Cabernet Sauvignon |
| Barrel ageing | 18 months - New barrels: 60% |
| Second wine | Cadet de Larmande |

Director: Bertrand de Villaines - Technical Manager: Véronique Corporandy - Communication: Caroline Rihouet - Vineyard Manager - Olivier Brunel

Château Larmande 1 Lieu-dit Soutard - 33330 Saint-Émilion
GPS: Latitude: 44.906376 - Longitude: -0.150173
Tel. +33 (0)5 57 24 71 41 - Fax +33 (0)5 57 74 42 80
contact@soutard.com - **www.chateau-soutard.com**

# CHÂTEAU PAVIE MACQUIN

## PREMIER GRAND CRU CLASSÉ

## SAINT-ÉMILION GRAND CRU

*Owner: the Corre-Macquin family*

PREMIER GRAND CRU CLASSÉ

*Famille Corre-Macquin*
*propriétaire*

This estate was founded by Albert Macquin (1852-1911), who studied viticulture at Paris-Grignon and Montpellier, and became a specialist in grafting and root stocks. Saint-Émilion can be grateful to him for introducing grafted vines, which saved the vineyards from ruin by phylloxera in the late 19th century.

Owned by the Corre-Macquin family, the vineyard has a prime location atop the plateau overlooking the limestone ledge of the Côte de Saint-Émilion. Facing westward, opposite the medieval town, Pavie Maquin overlooks the small Fongaban Valley.

The clay-limestone soil on asteriated limestone bedrock provides superb natural drainage and regular water supply. The high concentration of clay makes the wine strong, full-bodied, and generous.

One of Saint-Émilion's model châteaux, this beautiful estate uses traditional methods in the vineyard and cellar as well as selected modern techniques.

Origin can be beautiful, however, true beauty is in the conclusion of things...

| | |
|---|---|
| Area under vine | 15 hectares |
| Production | 50,000 bottles |
| Soil | Clay-limestone plateau |
| Grape varieties | 85% Merlot, 14% Cabernet franc, 1% Cabernet Sauvignon |
| Barrel ageing | 14-18 months - New barrels: 60% |
| Second wine | Les chênes de Macquin |

Estate Manager: Nicolas Thienpont - Consultant: Stéphane Derenoncourt

Château Pavie Macquin Peygenestau - 33330 Saint-Émilion
GPS: Latitude: 44.889952 - Longitude: -0.1465585
Tel. +33 (0)5 57 24 74 23 - Fax +33 (0)5 57 24 63 78
pavie-macquin@nicolas-thienpont.com - **www.pavie-macquin.com**

# CHÂTEAU SOUTARD
## GRAND CRU CLASSÉ

Soutard is a very ancient named place. The vineyard is located 800 metres as the crow flies from the steeple of Saint-Émilion's collegiate church, on the wonderful limestone plateau where most of the appellation's greatest wines are born.

Built in the 18th century, the château is located in the middle of the vines. It is truly the heart of the estate and overlooks the neighbouring valley.

The wines have a beautiful bouquet as well as great elegance, finesse, and power on the palate thanks to the magnificent terroir.

| | |
|---|---|
| Area under vine | 30 hectares |
| Production | 70,000 bottles |
| Soil | 70% limestone plateau, 17% clay-limestone slope, and 13% foot of the slope |
| Grape varieties | 63% Merlot, 28% Cabernet franc, 7% Cabernet Sauvignon, 2% Malbec |
| Barrel ageing | 18 months - New barrels: 60% |
| Second wine | Jardins de Soutard |

Director: Bertrand de Villaines - Winemaker: Véronique Corporandy - Communication: Caroline Rihouet
Vineyard Manager: Olivier Brunel

Château Soutard 1 Lieu-dit Soutard - 33330 Saint-Émilion
GPS: Latitude: 44.8983345- Longitude: -0.15008
Tel. +33 (0)5 57 24 71 41
contact@soutard.com - **www.chateau-soutard.com**

# CHÂTEAU LA TOUR FIGEAC
## GRAND CRU CLASSÉ

**SAINT-ÉMILION GRAND CRU** — *Owner: the Rettenmaier family*

Located on the famous terroir of the graves de Saint-Émilion bordering on Pomerol, this estate was separated from Château Figeac in 1879. La Tour Figeac was included as a Grand Cru Classé starting with the very first classification of Saint-Émilion in 1955.

The Rettenmaier family has owned and managed the estate since the early 1970s. The vines are tended and the wine made according not only to time-honoured Bordeaux traditions, but also to environmental protection and biodynamic principles. The estate produces its own compost, pigeage (punching down the cap) is practised, and many other natural methods are used.

Winemaking is adapted to the particularities of each vintage and benefits from the expertise of an experienced team, assisted by advice from Christine and Stéphane Derenoncourt, in order to fully reflect the fine terroir. La Tour Figeac is elegant, fruity, and attractively spicy, with hints of mint, eucalyptus, and violet.

| | |
|---|---|
| Area under vine | 14.5 hectares |
| Production | 40,000 bottles |
| Soil | Clay-sand and gravel |
| Grape varieties | 70% Merlot, 30% Cabernet franc |
| Barrel ageing | 15 months - New barrels: 50% |
| Second wine | L'Esquisse de La Tour Figeac |

Managing Director: Otto Rettenmaier

Château La Tour Figeac BP 007 - 33330 Saint-Émilion
GPS: Latitude: 44.9169843 - Longitude: -0.2011028
Tel. +33 (0)5 57 51 77 62 - Fax +33 (0)5 57 25 36 92
latourfigeac@orange.fr

# CHÂTEAU TROPLONG MONDOT

### PREMIER GRAND CRU CLASSÉ

## SAINT-ÉMILION GRAND CRU   *Owners: Christine and Xavier Pariente*

Domaine de Mondot belonged to Father de Sèze, who had the present-day château built in 1745. Under his management, the wine of Mondot became one of the most sought-after in Saint-Émilion.

Very much taken by the estate, Raymond Troplong purchased it in 1850 and constituted the vineyard as we know it today. Troplong was a French peer, famous lawyer, lover of art and literature, close friend of Théophile Gautier, and President of the French Senate from 1852 until his death in 1869. He succeeded in making the most of Mondot's fine terroir to produce superb wine that the 1868 edition of the famous Cocks and Féret (the "Bordeaux Bible") rated second best in Saint-Émilion. Before selling the estate, his nephew and heir, Édouard Troplong, added the family name.

Alexandre Valette, a wine merchant from Paris, acquired the property in the early 20th century. He already owned Château La France in Fronsac, another château of the same name in Quinsac, and acquired Château Pavie shortly thereafter. Alexandre's son, Bernard, followed by his grandson, Claude, followed in his footsteps as managers of the estate. Christine Valette-Pariente and her husband, Xavier Pariente, now own and operate Troplong Mondot.

| | |
|---|---|
| Area under vine | 28 hectares |
| Production | 85,000 bottles |
| Soil | Clay-limestone |
| Grape varieties | 90% Merlot, 8% Cabernet Sauvignon, 2% Cabernet franc |
| Barrel ageing | 12-24 months - New barrels: 85-100% |
| Second wine | Mondot |

Marketing and Communication: Myriam Ruer - Cellar Master: Jean-Pierre Taleyson - Vineyard Manager: Rémy Monribot

Château Troplong Mondot 1 Lieu dit Mondot 33330 Saint-Émilion
GPS: Latitude: 44.888895 - Longitude:-0.141445
Tel. +33 (0)5 57 55 32 05 - Fax +33 (0)5 57 55 32 07
contact@chateau-troplong-mondot.com - **www.chateau-troplong-mondot.com**

# CHÂTEAU TROTTEVIEILLE
## PREMIER GRAND CRU CLASSÉ

## SAINT-ÉMILION GRAND CRU

*Owner: the Casteja heirs*

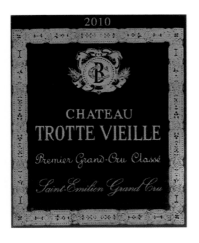

The name TrotteVieille comes from a legend having to do with an old lady who lived there centuries ago. A coach stop was located at the intersection of two roads just outside her house. Whenever a carriage stopped there, the old lady (la vieille) "trotted out" to hear all the latest news.

The second wine, La Dame de TrotteVieille, was created in 2002. A 15th century parchment written in Gascon proves that the name was already in use then.

The vineyard also has a very rare plot of pre-phylloxera vines. The grapes are handpicked into small crates and winemaking is always meticulous. Château TrotteVieille is known for its elegance, roundness, and very long aftertaste.

TrotteVieille has been a *Premier Grand Cru Classé* since the first classification of Saint-Emilion wines.

| | |
|---|---|
| Area under vine | 11 hectares |
| Soil | Limestone plateau covered with a thin layer of clay (about 30 centimetres) |
| Grape varieties | 50% Merlot, 45% Cabernet franc, 5% Cabernet Sauvignon |
| Barrel ageing | 12-18 months - New barrels: 100% |
| Second wine | Dame de TrotteVieille |

Director: Philippe Castéja

Château TrotteVieille 33330 Saint-Émilion
GPS: Latitude: 44.894522 - Longitude: -0.14544
Tel. +33 (0)5 56 00 00 70 - Fax +33 (0)5 57 87 48 61
domaines@borie-manoux.fr - www.trottevieille.com

# CHÂTEAU VILLEMAURINE

## GRAND CRU CLASSÉ

**CHÂTEAU VILLEMAURINE**

SAINT-EMILION GRAND CRU

*Grand Cru Classé*

Château Villemaurine, a Saint-Emilion Grand Cru Classé, is experiencing a veritable renaissance.

Fully aware of the care and respect required to restore a work of art, the Onclin family implemented a major upgrading programme to reveal the superb character of their terroir and to prepare the estate to receive visitors with a new ageing cellar and vat room, as well as renovating the underground cellars in a former quarry.

The vineyard, located on the Saint-Emilion clay-limestone plateau, is currently planted with 80% Merlot and 20% Cabernet Franc.

Justin Onclin's philosophy combines great respect for the terroir and an emphasis on excellence. Château Villemaurine has a remarkably long aftertaste, mineral overtones, and elegance, consistently expressing the subtle qualities of the best wines of Saint-Emilion, in keeping with an outstanding terroir. Villemaurine produces a second wine: les Angelots de Villemaurine.

| | |
|---|---|
| Area under vine | 7 hectares |
| Production | 30,000 bottles |
| Soil | Clay-limestone soil on a layer of asteriated limestone |
| Grape varieties | 80% Merlot, 20% Cabernet franc |
| Barrel ageing | 16 months - New barrels: 70% |
| Second wine | Les Angelots de Villemaurine |

Estate Manager: Carmen Onclin - Commercial Director: Cynthia Capelaere
Technical Director: Luc Pasqueron de Fommervault

Château Villemaurine Lieu-dit Villemaurine - 33330 Saint-Émilion
GPS: Latitude: 44,89 - Longitude: -0,15
Tel. +33 (0)5 57 74 47 30 - Fax +33 (0)5 57 24 63 09
contact@villemaurine.com - **www.villemaurine.com**

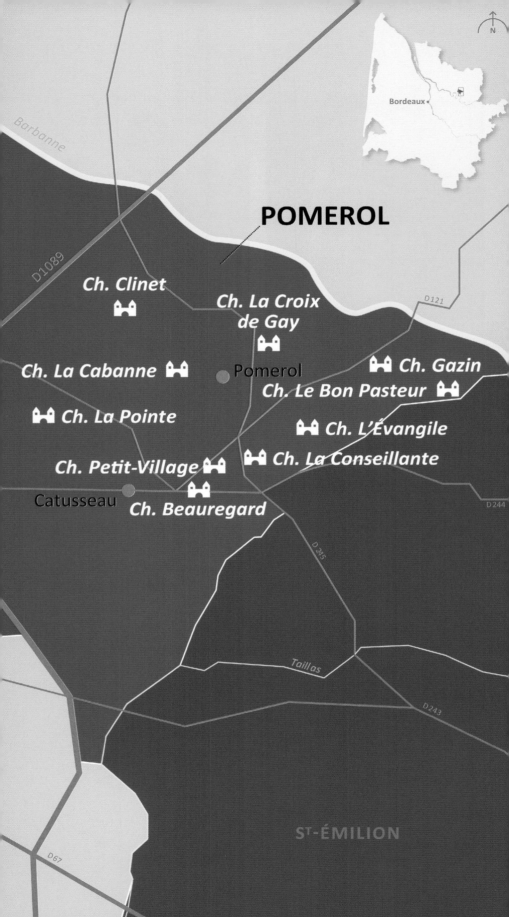

N

Bordeaux

**POMEROL**

Barbanne

D1089

D121

*Ch. Clinet*

*Ch. La Croix de Gay*

*Ch. La Cabanne*

Pomerol

*Ch. Gazin*

*Ch. Le Bon Pasteur*

*Ch. La Pointe*

*Ch. L'Évangile*

*Ch. Petit-Village*

*Ch. La Conseillante*

Catusseau

*Ch. Beauregard*

D244

D245

Taillas

D243

Sᵗ-ÉMILION

D67

# CRUS DE POMEROL

Located on the pilgrim road to Santiago de Compostela, the vineyards of Pomerol, which date back to Roman times, were developed by the Knights Templar. Although the Hundred Years' War brought only poverty and misery to the region, the vineyards once again thrived in the 15th and 16th centuries, and the reputation of their wines grew steadily.

In the 18th and 19th centuries, Pomerol's borders became more clearly defined, and the rarest wines were much sought after by buyers from around the world.

The major crises of the 20th century were overcome thanks to the devotion and commitment of winegrowers. The reputation of wines from this appellation has increased from year to year. Pomerol produces only a small quantity of wine so, historically, négociants and importers had to go there to sample and buy wines of the most recent vintage as soon as these were blended. This tradition has been maintained at the major tasting organised by the Union des Grands Crus de Bordeaux.

# CHÂTEAU BEAUREGARD

**POMEROL**

*Owner: Motier Domaines*

2014

CHATEAU
**BEAUREGARD**
POMEROL

Château Beauregard's history dates back to the 12th century. The Knights of Saint John of Jerusalem (the former name of the Knights of Malta) had a small manor house here which served as a stopover for pilgrims on the road to Santiago de Compostela. The Beauregard family built an impressive villa in the 17th century. This was in turn replaced by the present-day château designed by a student of Victor Louis, the architect responsible for Bordeaux's Grand Théâtre.

This elegant chartreuse, or stately home, bears witness to Beauregard's long history and its intrinsic charm and harmony. The estate has belonged to the Moulin and Cathiard families, longstanding friends, since July 2014. Their shared ambition is to give a new impetus to the château and build a state-of-the-art vat room and barrel cellar in time for the 2015 vintage. The aim is to achieve even greater precision in the winemaking and to make the most of Beauregard's outstanding terroir.

Château Beauregard is in an ideal location on the southern side of the famous Catusseau plateau in Pomerol and has a magnificent gravel and clay terroir. The château has an unusual blend of grape varieties, including some 30% Cabernet Franc. This variety is often discreet in its youth, but gains considerable freshness and elegance over time. Brilliantly fruity when young, Château Beauregard displays all the depth and smoothness of the great wines of Pomerol with age.

| | |
|---|---|
| Area under vine | 17.5 hectares |
| Production | 40,000 bottles |
| Soil | Gravel and clay |
| Grape varieties | 70% Merlot, 30% Cabernet franc |
| Barrel ageing | 18-22 months - New barrels: 50-60% |
| Second wine | Le Benjamin de Beauregard |

Joint Managing Directors: Augustin Belloy - Daniel Cathiard - Manager: Vincent Priou

Château Beauregard 33500 Pomerol
GPS: Latitude: 44.922527 - Longitude: -0.202003
Tel. +33 (0)5 57 51 13 36 - Fax +33 (0)5 57 25 09 55
pomerol@chateau-beauregard.com - **www.chateau-beauregard.com**

# CHÂTEAU LE BON PASTEUR

Owner: S.A.S. le Bon Pasteur

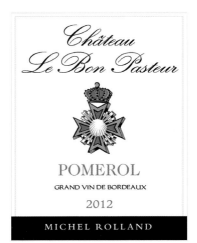

Located in the Maillet sector, at the junction of the famous terroirs of Pomerol and Saint-Émilion, Château Le Bon Pasteur was created by Joseph and Hermine Dupuy, parents of Genevieve Rolland and grandparents of Jean-Daniel and Michel Rolland. This small estate, acquired circa 1920, gradually expanded and attained its present size in 1955.

It goes without saying that Le Bon Pasteur benefits from the winemaking philosophy and experience of the well-known oenologists Dany and Michel Rolland, who created a model vineyard and a wine of great class. The grapes in each plot are picked at ideal ripeness and carefully sorted. They are then separately fermented in new barrels or small temperature-controlled vats (15-70 hl). Pressing is gentle and winemaking as non-interventionist as possible in order to retain the specific characteristics of each plot and grape variety throughout barrel ageing and until the final blend is made.

The diversity of plots explains the complexity and originality of this wine from beginning to end. Furthermore it is not fined before bottling. Thanks to the experience of the famous oenologists Dany and Michel Rolland, Château Le Bon Pasteur is one of the gems of Pomerol, a fine wine recognized by critics around the world.

Château Le Bon Pasteur has belonged to the Goldin group since June 2013. It is managed by Benoît Prévot, although the existing winemaking team was maintained to benefit from, and perpetuate their expertise.

| | |
|---|---|
| Area under vine | 7 hectares |
| Production | 25,000 bottles |
| Soil | Clay-gravel, gravel and sand |
| Grape varieties | 80% Merlot, 20% Cabernet franc |
| Barrel ageing | 15-18 months - New barrels: 100% |

Consultant: Michel Rolland - Managing Director: Benoît Prévot - Brand Ambassador: Dany Rolland

Château Le Bon Pasteur Maillet 33500 Pomerol
GPS: Latitude: 44.929329 - Longitude: -0.180995
Tel. +33 (0)5 57 24 52 58 - Fax +33 (0)5 57 25 36 39
contact@chateaulebonpasteur.com - **www.chateaulebonpasteur.com**

# CHÂTEAU LA CABANNE

Owned by the Jean-Pierre Estager family, Château La Cabanne is located in the heart of Pomerol.

Although vines have been grown here since Gallo-Roman times, the name goes back to the 14th century, when serfs who worked in the vineyard lived in cabins ("cabanes").

A dynamic estate, Château La Cabanne regularly updates their winemaking equipment (which was totally replaced in 2011 after a fire destroyed the vat room), while gradually restructuring the vineyard.

Viticultural practices combine both a traditional and modern approach, and are done in keeping with the appellation's highest standards.

Château La Cabanne is a well-balanced wine, with an intense, complex nose showing hints of blackberry jam, raspberry and toasted bread. Silky tannin on the palate provides volume and density, and there is a long aftertaste. Undergoing rigorous blending, La Cabanne ranks among the greatest Pomerols.

Château La Cabanne also produces a second wine, Domaine de Compostelle, mainly from young vines.

| | |
|---|---|
| Area under vine | 10 hectares |
| Production | 36,000 bottles |
| Soil | Clay-gravel with a subsoil rich in crasse de fer (ironpan) |
| Grape varieties | 94% Merlot, 6% Cabernet franc |
| Barrel ageing | 15 months - New barrels: 60% |
| Second wine | Domaine de Compostelle |

Manager: Michèle Estager - Managing Director: François Estager - Technical Director: Florent Faure

Château La Cabanne 2, chemin de la Cabanne - 33500 Pomerol
GPS: Latitude: 44.93194 - Longitude: -0.21
Tel. +33 (0)5 57 51 04 09 - Fax +33 (0)5 57 25 13 38
estager@estager.com - **www.estager.com**

# CHÂTEAU CLINET

*Owner: Ronan Laborde*

2012

**CHÂTEAU**

# CLINET

*Pomerol*

Listed as a 1st growth of Pomerol in 1893, Château Clinet's history goes back to the 17th century.

The estate was acquired in 1998 by Jean-Louis Laborde, and is now managed by Ronan Laborde.

Located on the highest part of the famous Pomerol plateau, Clinet has an outstanding terroir. The vines are grown sustainably and most operations are done by hand.

The underground cellar enables winemaking operations to be performed with gravity flow, and to make the wine as naturally as possible.

It ages in oak barrels and is neither fined nor filtered before bottling.

Château Clinet is an elegant, intense, refined wine with complex aromas of red fruit, blackberry, and truffle.

| | |
|---|---|
| Area under vine | 11.3 hectares |
| Production | 45,000 bottles |
| Soil | Clay and gravel |
| Grape varieties | 90% Merlot, 9% Cabernet Sauvignon, 1% Cabernet franc |
| Barrel ageing | 16 months - New barrels: 50% |
| Second wine | Fleur de Clinet |

Sales and marketing: Monique Bailly - Tours: Marie-Céline Wallerand

Château Clinet 16 chemin de Feytit - 33500 Pomerol
GPS: Latitude: 44.93389 - Longitude: -0.205189
Tel. +33 (0)5 57 25 50 00 - Fax +33 (0)5 57 25 70 00
contact@chateauclinet.com - **www.chateauclinet.com**

# CHÂTEAU LA CONSEILLANTE

Owner: the Nicolas family

The first recorded history of La Conseillante's name appears in the mid-18th century. It was bequeathed by an influential woman who owned the estate almost 300 years ago: Catherine Conseillan.

The Nicolas family bought the château in 1871, and its size and configuration have not changed ever since. Exemplifying the Nicolas family's continued commitment to this great wine, the fifth generation is currently at the helm.

Located on the heart of the famous Pomerol plateau next to its renowned neighbours, Pétrus and Cheval Blanc, La Conseillante has an outstanding terroir. Its full potential has been achieved, and the wine has gained a well-deserved reputation for power and elegance.

La Conseillante's silky tannin, aromatic complexity, and regularity year in and year out account for its loyal following around the world.

| | |
|---|---|
| Area under vine | 11.8 hectares |
| Production | 45,000 bottles |
| Soil | Clay and gravel over *crasse de fer* (ironpan) in the subsoil |
| Grape varieties | 80% Merlot, 20% Cabernet franc |
| Barrel ageing | 18 months - New barrels: 50-75% |
| Second wine | Duo de Conseillante |

Director: Marielle Cazaux - Co-Manager: Bertrand Nicolas - Co-Manager: Valmy Nicolas

Château La Conseillante 33500 Pomerol
GPS: Latitude: 44.924247 - Longitude: -0.194814
Tel. +33 (0)5 57 51 15 32 - Fax +33 (0)5 57 51 42 39
contact@la-conseillante.com - **www.la-conseillante.com**

# CHÂTEAU LA CROIX DE GAY

　　　　　　　　　　　　　*Owner: Chantal Lebreton*

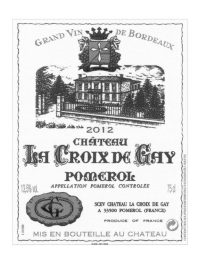

Château La Croix de Gay is located in the historic heart of Pomerol, with family roots in Pomerol going back to 1477.

The 4.2-hectare vineyard is evenly divided between two types of soil: Günz gravel on the upper Pomerol terrace and the southern slope of the plateau. Each of these two terroirs confers distinct characteristics to Merlot and Cabernet Franc grapes that contribute to the complexity of the final blend.

The new vat room has been in use since the 2014 vintage and operates uniquely by gravity flow. Fermentation and maceration take place in cement vats, which feature great thermal inertia. The capacity of these unusual small tulip-shaped vats corresponds perfectly to the grapes from each individual plot.

Chantal Lebreton-Raynaud is presently in charge of the estate, guaranteeing that that wine she produces is in keeping with its status of "veritable ferruginous nectar" – as per the 1929 edition of the Cocks & Féret ("Bordeaux and its Wines"). This is an allusion to a major characteristic of Pomerol's terroir (ironpan) that gives the wine roundness, makes it approachable young, and contributes typical aromas such as violet and truffle.

| | |
|---|---|
| Area under vine | 4.20 hectares |
| Production | 20,000 bottles |
| Soil | Clayey-gravel and sandy-gravel overlaying a subsoil rich in ironpan |
| Grape varieties | 98% Merlot, 2% Cabernet franc |
| Barrel ageing | 18 months - New barrels: 50% |

Château La Croix de Gay 8, chemin de Saint-Jacques de Compostelle, Lieu-dit Pignon - 33500 Pomerol
GPS: Latitude: 44.93518 - Longitude: - 0.199422
Tel. +33 (0)5 57 51 19 05 - Fax. +33 (0)5 57 51 81 81
contact@chateau-lacroixdegay.com – **www.chateau-lacroixdegay.com**

77

# CHÂTEAU L'ÉVANGILE

Owner: Domaines Barons de Rothschild (Lafite)

MIS EN BOUTEILLE AU CHÂTEAU

2010

CHATEAU

L' ÉVANGILE

POMEROL

Due to a curious geological anomaly, a long strip of gravel was formed on the southeastern part of the Pomerol plateau. Three vineyards, including L'Évangile, share this rare terroir. The estate is bordered to the north by Pétrus, and is only separated from Cheval Blanc to the south (in the Saint-Émilion appellation) by a country road.

The property was constituted in the 18th century by the Léglise family and was renamed L'Évangile at the turn of the 19th century.

In 1862, L'Évangile was acquired by Paul Chaperon, whose heirs, the Ducasse family, were owners until 1990. As early as 1868, it was considered the Premier Cru du Haut Pomerol (2nd edition of Cocks and Féret).

Domaines Barons de Rothschild (Lafite) acquired Château L'Évangile in 1990. The first manifestation of their influence was a more rigorous selection for the grand vin and the creation of a second wine, Blason de L'Évangile. A vineyard replanting programme was also initiated in 1998. The new configuration was finalised in 2004 with the renovation of the vat room and cellars. These efforts have been conducive to a decade of remarkable vintages.

| | |
|---|---|
| Area under vine | 22 hectares |
| Production | 24-36,000 bottles |
| Soil | Sand and clay with pure gravel and a subsoil with *crasse de fer* (ironpan) |
| Grape varieties | 90% Merlot, 20% Cabernet franc |
| Barrel ageing | 18 months - New barrels: 70% |
| Second wine | Blason de L'Évangile |

Château L'Évangile 33500 Pomerol
GPS: Latitude: 44.926133 - Longitude: -0.192375
Tel. +33 (0)5 57 55 45 55 - Fax +33 (0)5 57 55 45 56
levangile@lafite.com - **www.lafite.com**

# CHÂTEAU GAZIN

POMEROL                    *Owner: the de Bailliencourt dit Courcol family*

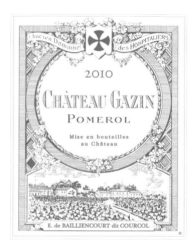

Château Gazin formerly belonged to the Knights of Saint John of Jerusalem (the Order of Malta) and is one of the largest estates in its appellation. The vineyard is in a single block on the upper part of the famous Pomerol plateau.

Gazin is currently owned by the Bailliencourt family. Descended from the Lords of Landas, the Bailliencourt dit Courcol family is one of the oldest in the province of Artois. The name Courcol (meaning "short collar") was given to an ancestor by Philippe Auguste, King of France during the battle of Bouvines in 1214 due to his bravery in time of war. Louis Soualle, the great-grandfather of the present owners, acquired Château Gazin in the early 20th century and the estate continues to be carefully managed by his descendants.

The grapes are fermented in concrete vats and malolactic fermentation takes place in barrel, after which the wine is also aged in oak. It is then fined with egg whites and, if need be, lightly filtered before bottling at the château. Annual production (85% exported) can attain up to 100,000 bottles (including 30,000 for the second wine). Château Gazin belongs to the Académie du Vin de Bordeaux.

| | |
|---|---|
| Area under vine | 24.24 hectares |
| Production | 70,000 bottles |
| Soil | Clay-gravel with *crasse de fer* (ironpan) |
| Grape varieties | 90% Merlot, 7% Cabernet Sauvignon, 3% Cabernet franc |
| Barrel ageing | 18 months - New barrels: 50% |
| Second wine | L'Hospitalet de Gazin |

Managing Director (G.F.A.): Christophe de Bailliencourt dit Courcol
Managing Director (S.C.E.A.): Nicolas de Bailliencourt dit Courcol - Director: Mickaël Obert

Château Gazin 1 chemin de Chantecaille - 33500 Pomerol
GPS: Latitude: 44.930614 - Longitude: -0.188231
Tel. +33 (0)5 57 51 07 05 - Fax +33 (0)5 57 51 69 96
contact@gazin.com - **www.gazin.com**

# CHÂTEAU PETIT-VILLAGE

*Owner: AXA Millésimes*

GRAND VIN DU

## Château
# Petit-Village

### 2012

## POMEROL

Château Petit-Village is located on the highest point of the gravel plateau in the heart of the Pomerol appellation. The 10.5 hectares vineyard is in a single triangular-shaped plot.

Combining age-old vine-growing traditions with modern facilities of the highest standard – that is the challenge we set ourselves at Château Petit-Village. Today, the vast labours of restructuring the vineyard and renovating the winery facilities are bearing fruit.

Each and every step in the process that leads through to bottling, from picking the grapes by hand to allowing the wine to rest in oak casks, is guided by our respect for the terroir in its fullest expression.

The wines of Château Petit-Village are fresh and balanced with remarkable intensity of fruit and all the incomparable richness and finesse of the greatest wines of Pomerol.

| | |
|---|---|
| Area under vine | 10.5 hectares |
| Production | 30,000 bottles |
| Soil | Deep gravel with light sandy clay over a subsoil of *crasse de fer* (iron pan) |
| Grape varieties | 75% Merlot, 18% Cabernet franc, 7% Cabernet Sauvignon |
| Barrel ageing | 15 months - New barrels: 60-70% |
| Second wine | Le Jardin de Petit-Village |

Managing Director: Christian Seely

Château Petit-Village 126 route de Catusseau - 33500 Pomerol
GPS: Latitude: 44.923913 - Longitude: -0.200393
Tel. +33 (0)5 57 51 21 08 - Fax +33 (0)5 57 51 87 31
contact@petit-village.com - **www.petit-village.com**

# CHÂTEAU LA POINTE

*Owner: S.C.E. Château La Pointe*

Château La Pointe's lovely 2 hectares of grounds and centuries-old trees have made this an outstandingly beautiful property for over a century and a half. It gained recognition as an important winegrowing estate in the 19th century.

One of the largest vineyards in Pomerol, La Pointe underwent a major renovation starting in 2008 in order to enhance its image and achieve the terroir's full potential.

A detailed soil survey made it possible to maximise drainage and restructure the vineyards in the interest of quality. The Cabernet Sauvignon vines were uprooted and the yields of Cabernet Franc adapted in order to express the finesse and elegance that make La Pointe one of the mostly highly-reputed wines on the Right Bank.

A major renovation of the cellars was also undertaken. This makes it possible to ferment grapes from each plot separately to fine-tune winemaking, as well as respect stringent environmental standards.

The internationally respected consultant, Hubert de Boüard de Laforest, co-owner of Château Angélus, now shares his expertise with the Château La Pointe team.

| | |
|---|---|
| Area under vine | 23 hectares |
| Production | 100,000 bottles |
| Soil | Gravel and river stones deposited by the Isle River, clay limestone soil, sand on clay, and clay on gravel |
| Grape varieties | Red wine: 85% Merlot, 15% Cabernet franc |
| Barrel ageing | 12 months - New barrels: 50% |
| Second wine | Ballade de La Pointe |

Managing Director: Éric Monneret - Consultant: Hubert de Boüard de Laforest - Technical Director: Émilie Faniest

Château La Pointe 33500 Pomerol
GPS: Latitude: 44.92555 - Longitude: -0.21685
Tel. +33 (0)5 57 51 02 11 - Fax +33 (0)5 57 51 42 33
contact@chateaulapointe.com - **www.chateaulapointe.com**

81

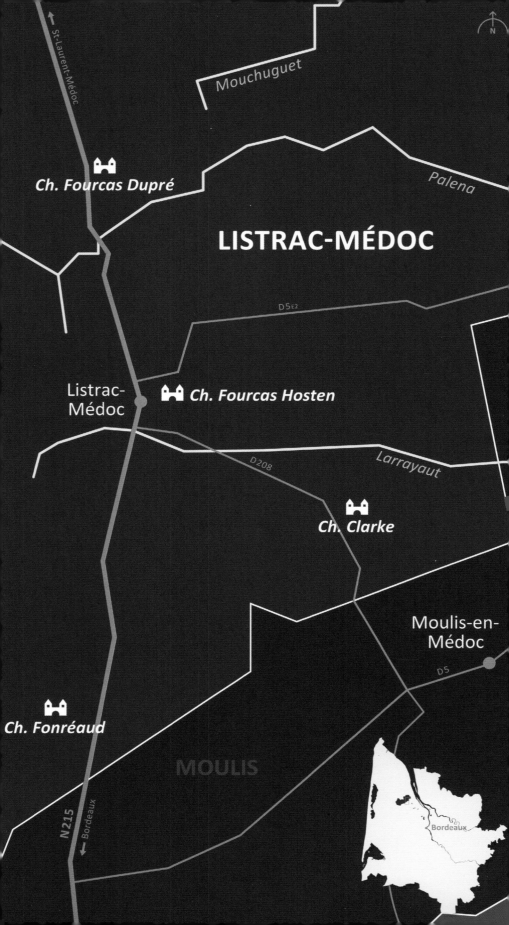

St-Laurent-Médoc

Mouchuguet

Palena

Ch. Fourcas Dupré

**LISTRAC-MÉDOC**

D5ᴇ2

Listrac-
Médoc

Ch. Fourcas Hosten

D208

Larrayaut

Ch. Clarke

Moulis-en-
Médoc

D5

Ch. Fonréaud

MOULIS

N215

Bordeaux

Bordeaux

N

# CRUS DE LISTRAC-MÉDOC

This wine-producing commune has been famous since the late 18th century. *Le Producteur*, a publication targeting the Bordeaux wine industry, noted as early as 1838 that vineyard owners in Listrac were able to overcome numerous challenges to make a name for themselves thanks to the unique quality of their wines.

This quality was acknowledged in the early 20th century when the appellation contrôlée system was first established, although separate status was granted somewhat later than other Médoc communes, in June 1957, when Listrac-Médoc was officially entitled to its own appellation. Three years after Margaux, it became the youngest communal appellation in Bordeaux.

# CHÂTEAU CLARKE
## BARON EDMOND DE ROTHSCHILD

**LISTRAC-MÉDOC**                    *Owner: Baron Benjamin de Rothschild*

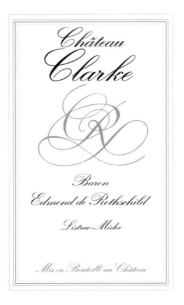

Château Clarke is named after an Irish family who acquired the estate in the 18th century. Clarke was purchased by Baron Edmond de Rothschild in 1973 and entirely renovated. The vineyard currently consists of fifty-five hectares of clay-limestone rises ideally suited to Merlot, which is by far the most widely-planted variety (a fairly rare situation in the Médoc).

Methods such as hand picking into small crates, meticulous sorting in the cellar, and the use of gravity flow are perfectly adapted to recently-constructed winemaking facilities and an unfailing emphasis on quality.

The magnificent 4-hectare gardens surrounding Château Clarke feature an amazingly diverse selection of plants and trees which are looked after with the same care and attention as the vines and wine.

Since 1997, Baron Benjamin de Rothschild and his wife, Ariane, have been in charge of the estate, helping to motivate a dynamic winemaking team with their quest for excellence in keeping with the vision of the late Baron Edmond de Rothschild.

| | |
|---|---|
| Area under vine | 55 hectares |
| Production | 250,000 bottles |
| Soil | Clay-limestone |
| Grape varieties | 70% Merlot, 30% Cabernet Sauvignon |
| Barrel ageing | 16-18 months - New barrels: 60% |
| Second wine | Les Granges des Domaines Edmond de Rothschild |

Managing Director: Georges Alnot - Technical Director: Yann Buchwalter
Commercial Director: Hélène Combabessouse

Château Clarke 33480 Listrac-Médoc
GPS: Latitude: 45.0661156 - Longitude: -0.7735646
Tel. +33 (0)5 56 58 38 00 - Fax +33 (0)5 56 58 26 46
contact@cver.fr - **www.cver.fr**

# CHÂTEAU FONRÉAUD

The Château is well-known for its historic vineyard and the quality of its wines. Its name comes from a legend, and the attractive château enjoys a privileged location on the highest point in the Médoc.

Fonréaud, was formerly called Font-réaux, meaning "royal fountain". A legend tells us that in the 12th century, the King of England (probably Henry II Plantagenet, the husband of Eleanor of Aquitaine) quenched his thirst from a spring he found on the grounds.

Thanks to a subtle blend of grape varieties, the terroir comes through beautifully in round wines with ripe tannin, fine structure and a velvety texture that develops beautifully on the palate.

The vat room houses small temperature-controlled vats that allow grapes from each plot to express their nuances, and also make it possible to fine-tune the final blend.

Aged in barrel, the elegance and charm of this fine wine reflect the spirit of the Chanfreau family.

| | |
|---|---|
| Area under vine | 38 hectares |
| Production | 150,000 Bottles |
| Soil | Pyrenean gravel with a clay-limestone subsoil |
| Grape varieties | 53% Cabernet Sauvignon, 43% Merlot, 4% Petit Verdot |
| Barrel ageing | 12 months - New barrels: 33% |
| Second wine | La Légende de Fonréaud |

Manager: Jean Chanfreau

Château Fonréaud 33480 Listrac-Médoc
GPS: Latitude: 45.05775 - Longitude: -0.797389
Tel. +33 (0)5 56 58 02 43 - Fax +33 (0)5 56 58 04 33
contact@vignobles-chanfreau.com - **www.chateau-fonreaud.com**

# CHÂTEAU FOURCAS DUPRÉ

*Owner: S.C.E. du Château Fourcas Dupré*

Vines have grown in "Fourcas" since the early 18th century, as proved by royal cartographers Masse, Robert, Belleyme, etc. Situated at an altitude of 42 metres, the Fourcas plateau is called the "roof of the Médoc" and features the oldest geological stratum in the region. Formerly called "cru Roullet", Fourcas Dupré took on its present name in 1843 when Jean-Antoine Baptiste Dupré, a Bordeaux solicitor, acquired the estate.

In 1970, Guy Pagès bought the château and undertook a major renovation, transforming Fourcas Dupré in the process into one of the finest wines in its appellation. His son, Patrice Pagès, took over in 1985, perpetuating the same meticulousness, expertise, and passion. Château Fourcas Dupré's terroir is an unusual blend of gravel, clay, and limestone. It is one of the rare estates in the Médoc with more than 80% Pyrenean gravel, which accounts for the wine's strong personality.

Thanks to this soil and carefully-studied proportions of grape varieties, the wines of Fourcas Dupré reflect their terroir with great success. Mineral, complex, and very expressive on the palate, they also have tremendous ageing potential.

| | |
|---|---|
| Area under vine | 46 hectares |
| Production | 200,000 bottles |
| Soil | Pyrenean gravel, with a clay-limestone subsoil |
| Grape varieties | 44% Merlot, 44% Cabernet Sauvignon, 10% Cabernet franc, 2% Petit Verdot |
| Barrel ageing | 12 months - New barrels: 33% |
| Second wine | Bellevue de Fourcas Dupré |

Manager: Patrice Pagès

Château Fourcas Dupré Le Fourcas - 33480 Listrac-Médoc
GPS: Latitude: 45.087502 - Longitude: -0.796587
Tel. +33 (0)5 56 58 01 07 - Fax +33 (0)5 56 58 02 27
info@fourcasdupre.com - **www.fourcasdupre.com**

# CHÂTEAU FOURCAS HOSTEN

*Owners: Renaud and Laurent Momméja*

GRAND VIN DE BORDEAUX

Thanks to a highly unusual terroir that accounts for the wine's subtle balance, Château Fourcas Hosten has enjoyed a fine reputation for nearly two hundred years.

Located in the heart of the village of Listrac, in the middle of 3-hectare English-style grounds, the 18th century country manor house overlooks a clay-limestone plain where Merlot grapes express all their goodness. Further north, Cabernet Sauvignon vines are very much at home on the gravel soil of the plateau de Fourcas.

While making sure to respect centuries-old traditions and longstanding Médoc winemaking expertise, the new owners, Renaud and Laurent Momméja, are also committed to providing the most up-to-date facilities and techniques. Everything possible is done to express the character and elegance of Fourcas Hosten.

| | |
|---|---|
| Area under vine | 36 hectares |
| Production | 150,000 bottles |
| Soil | 50% Pyrenean gravel and 50% clay-limestone |
| Grape varieties | 53% Merlot, 44% Cabernet Sauvignon, 3% Cabernet franc |
| Barrel ageing | 12 months - New barrels:35% |
| Second wine | Les Cèdres d'Hosten |

Managing Director: Renaud Momméja - Technical and Administrative Director: Caroline Artaud - Sales and Marketing Manager: Sophie Solnicki-Thierry

**Château Fourcas Hosten** 5 rue Odilon Redon - 33480 Listrac-Médoc
GPS: Latitude: 45.075915 - Longitude: -0.790003
Tel. +33 (0)5 56 58 01 15 - Fax +33 (0)5 56 58 06 73
contact@fourcas-hosten.com - **www.fourcas-hosten.com**

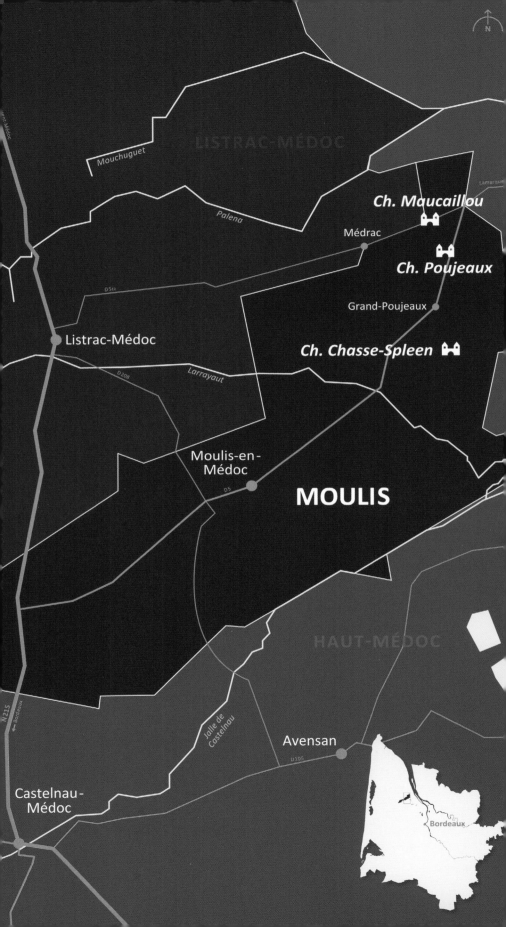

N

LISTRAC-MÉDOC

Mouchuguet

Palena

Ch. Maucaillou

Médrac

Ch. Poujeaux

Grand-Poujeaux

D 5₁₂

Lamarque

Ch. Chasse-Spleen

Listrac-Médoc

D 208

Larrayaut

Moulis-en-Médoc

**MOULIS**

D 5

HAUT-MÉDOC

N 215

Bordeaux

Jalle de Castelnau

Avensan

D 105

Castelnau-Médoc

Bordeaux

# CRUS DE MOULIS-EN-MÉDOC

The commune of Moulis, and thus the wine appellation, are named after the numerous moulins, or mills (both water and wind-powered) found there at one time. Moulis is a deformation of the words *molinis* and *mola* of Latin origin. While this name proves that grain was grown in the region, we also know that vines were cultivated here as far back as the Middle Ages by several vineyard owners and a large religious community. The winegrowing commune of Moulis is probably one of the oldest in the Médoc. Bearing witness to a prestigious past, the town also has one of the most beautiful Romanesque churches in the entire region.

The vineyards of Moulis and the reputation of its wines greatly developed during the 18th and 19th centuries, at the same time as other neighbouring communes.

# CHÂTEAU CHASSE-SPLEEN

*Owner: Céline Villars-Foubet*

Some people attribute the name of this château to Lord Byron during a trip he made to France, whereas others credit Charles Baudelaire while visiting his artist friend Odilon Redon, a neighbour of Chasse Spleen and illustrator of "Spleen et Idéal".

The estate has been managed by women for the past thirty years: Jacques Merlaut's daughter, Bernadette Villars, starting in 1976, followed by her daughter, Claire, beginning in 1992, and now her sister, Céline.

The vineyard is located in Moulis, the smallest appellation in the Médoc, just off the Route des Châteaux, halfway between Margaux and Saint-Julien. Its extraordinarily varied terroir consists of complementary soil types going from pure Garonne and Pyrenean gravel to a mixture of clay and limestone.

Chasse-Spleen reflects this diversity and the best of its appellation thanks to the fresh, mineral qualities of Cabernet Sauvignon grown on a thick layer of gravel and the roundness and smoothness of Merlot planted on largely clay-limestone soil.

| | |
|---|---|
| Area under vine | 92 hectares |
| Production | 400,000 bottles |
| Soil | Garonne gravel, Asteriated limestone subsoil |
| Grape varieties | 65% Cabernet Sauvignon, 30% Merlot, 5% Petit Verdot |
| Barrel ageing | 18 months - New barrels: 40% |
| Second wine | Oratoire de Chasse-Spleen |

Office/tours: Odile Bouchereau - Group tours: Jennifer Pomiès

Château Chasse-Spleen 32 chemin de la raze - 33480 Moulis-en-Médoc
GPS: Latitude: 45.0737881- Longitude: -0.7409932
Tel. +33 (0)5 56 58 02 37 - Fax +33 (0)5 57 88 84 40
info@chasse-spleen.com - **www.chasse-spleen.com**

# CHÂTEAU MAUCAILLOU

*Owner: S.A.S. Château Maucaillou*

Coinciding with a veritable family saga, Château Maucaillou's history reflects both patience and passion. The château was built in 1875 in a very Baroque style that was popular at the time. It was surrounded by five hectares of vines.

The Dourthe brothers, Roger and André, devoted their efforts to expanding the vineyard when they arrived at the estate in 1929, succeeding in attaining twenty hectares in 1967. At this point, Roger's son, Philippe, became manager. He added a further 67 hectares over a forty-year period, including vines on the three finest rises in Moulis. In 2007, Philippe Dourthe handed over management to his children Caroline, Pascal, and Magali. A fully-qualified team respectful of the Dourthe winemaking philosophy is now in control. A draconian selection at harvest time, precision winemaking in temperature-controlled vats, and careful ageing in barrel produce wines with a sumptuous colour, as well as rich, concentrated aromas, subtle tannin, and an astonishingly long aftertaste.

Château Maucaillou has won numerous medals and regularly receives good reviews from critics.

| | |
|---|---|
| Area under vine | 87 hectares |
| Production | 300,000 bottles |
| Soil | 75% Günz gravel and 25% clay-limestone |
| Grape varieties | 51% Cabernet Sauvignon, 42% Merlot, 7% Petit Verdot |
| Barrel ageing | 14-16 months - New barrels: 30-40% |
| Second wine | Numéro 2 de Maucaillou |

President of the Board of Directors: Pascal Dourthe - Technical Director: Magali Dourthe
Director of Communication: Cyril Forget

Château Maucaillou 33480 Moulis-en-Médoc
GPS: Latitude: 45.0857059 - Longitude: -0.7447877
Tel. +33 (0)5 56 58 01 23 - Fax +33 (0)5 56 58 00 88
chateau@maucaillou.com - **www.maucaillou.com**

# CHÂTEAU POUJEAUX

**MOULIS-EN-MÉDOC**   *Owner: the Cuvelier family*

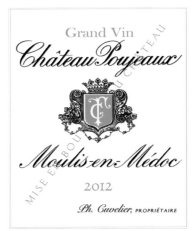

Winegrowing at Château Poujeaux dates from the 19th century, although it was a seigneury owing allegiance to Latour Saint Mambert, the future Château Latour, in the Middle Ages... A period of prosperity was followed by an unsettled time with many different owners, and the vineyard was broken up in the early 20th century. Fortunately, it was reconsolidated by the Theil family, who did much to give the wine a fine reputation.

In January 2008, Château Poujeaux was purchased by the Cuvelier family (who were already the proud owners of Clos Fourtet, a Premier Grand Cru Classé of Saint-Emilion). This was the beginning of a new chapter in Poujeaux's history. Philippe Cuvelier and his son, Matthieu, asked Stéphane Derenoncourt to advise them, while retaining the existing winemaking team. This is headed by Christophe Labenne, the grandson of the former owners.

While perpetuating the wine's generous, yet delicate style, the new orientation is toward better focus in order to bring Poujeaux up to its ultimate potential. The vines grow in a single block on a great terroir in the heart of the Médoc: a beautiful gravelly rise in Grand-Poujeaux.

| | |
|---|---|
| Area under vine | 63 hectares |
| Production | 250,000 bottles |
| Soil | Günz gravel |
| Grape varieties | 50% Cabernet Sauvignon, 40% Merlot, 5% Cabernet franc, 5% Petit Verdot |
| Barrel ageing | 12 months - New barrels: 30% |
| Second wine | La Salle de Château Poujeaux |

Estate Manager: Matthieu Cuvelier - Director: Christophe Labenne

Château Poujeaux 450 avenue de la Gironde 33480 Moulis-en-Médoc
GPS: Latitude: 45.079512- Longitude: -0.743057
Tel. +33 (0)5 56 58 02 96 - Fax +33 (0)5 56 58 01 25
contact@chateau-poujeaux.com - **www.chateau-poujeaux.com**

Ch. Coufran

St-Seurin-
de-Cardourne

MÉDOC

Gironde

SAINT-ESTÈPHE

Île de
Patiras

PAUILLAC

Pauillac

Île
Bouchaud

St-Julien
Beychevelle

Ch. Belgrave

St-Laurent-
Médoc

SAINT-JULIEN

Beychevelle

Ch. La Tour
Carnet

Ch. de
Camensac

HAUT-MÉDOC

Île
Nouvelle

Ch. Beaumont

Ch. de Lamarque

LISTRAC-MÉDOC

Lamarque

Île
Verte

Listrac-Médoc

Moulis-en-Médoc

Ch. Citran

MOULIS

Margaux

Castelnau-
Médoc

Ch. Cantemerle

Ludon-Médoc

Ch. La Lagune

N

Bordeaux

# CRUS DE HAUT-MÉDOC

The Haut-Médoc stretches northwest of Bordeaux, from a stream called the Jalle de Blanquefort to the commune of Saint-Seurin-de-Cadourne. These boundaries had been defined for many years, and wines from this region have a long-established reputation. The part of the Médoc located closest to the city of Bordeaux, its vast terroir has produced fine wine since the 17th century. The owners of large estates made the most of their privileged location close to the port of Bordeaux and major transportation routes to export their wines all over the world. The northernmost vineyards were mostly created in the latter half of the 19th century.

# CHÂTEAU BEAUMONT

*Owner: Grands Millésimes de France (Castel & Suntory)*

Winegrowing at Château Beaumont dates back to 1824. The present château, a pure jewel of Mansart-style architecture, was built in 1854. Its exotic history includes an unusual collection of characters: a Breton aristocrat, a Honduran minister, a Parisian industrialist, a lieutenant-colonel from Caracas, a Venezuelan senator, etc. – twelve different owners who ensured that Beaumont was enjoyed around the world.

Currently owned by Grands Millésimes de France, Château Beaumont produces an elegant, concentrated, well-balanced wine with beautiful colour, extreme finesse, an exquisite bouquet, and a silky texture.

Committed to ecological concerns for several years, Château Beaumont obtained certification for sustainable viticulture from the Terra Vitis organization in 2004 after conforming to a set of stringent specifications involving close observation and respect for the environment.

| | |
|---|---|
| Area under vine | 114 hectares |
| Production | 480,000 bottles |
| Soil | A rise consisting of Günz gravel and sand |
| Grape varieties | 47% Cabernet Sauvignon, 45% Merlot, 8% Petit Verdot |
| Barrel ageing | 14 months - New barrels: 30% |
| Second wine | Château d'Arvigny |

Director: Étienne Priou - Manager: Philippe Blanc

Château Beaumont 33460 Cussac-Fort-Médoc
GPS: Latitude: 45.108643 - Longitude: -0.73088
Tel. +33 (0)5 56 58 92 29 - Fax +33 (0)5 56 58 90 94
beaumont@chateau-beaumont.com - **www.chateau-beaumont.com**

# CHÂTEAU BELGRAVE
## GRAND CRU CLASSÉ EN 1855

## HAUT-MÉDOC

Included as a 5th growth in the 1855 classification thanks to the quality of its deep gravel soil, Château Belgrave has been managed by Dourthe since 1979. An attractive 18th century hunting lodge surrounded by sixty hectares of vines in a single block, Belgrave is located in the commune of Saint-Laurent, separated from the Saint-Julien appellation only by a small stream.

A great deal of work, passion, and energy have gone into producing wines worthy of one of the finest terroirs in the Médoc. The vineyard has been entirely renovated and is looked after with great care and attention.

Benefiting from experience acquired by Dourthe at their various estates, the ripe, healthy grapes are fermented in a vat room featuring the latest technological advances.

The ageing cellar was also refurbished in an unabashedly mordern style epitomising the rebirth of the estate. Thanks to this in-depth modernisation and expert care, Château Belgrave is now among the elite of Médoc great growths.

| | |
|---|---|
| Area under vine | 59 hectares |
| Production | 250,000 bottles |
| Soil | Deep gravel with a clay subsoil |
| Grape varieties | 50% Merlot, 46% Cabernet Sauvignon, and 4% Petit Verdot |
| Barrel ageing | 12-14 months - New barrels: 35-45% |
| Second wine | Diane de Belgrave |

Manager: Vignobles Dourthe - President: Patrick Jestin - Director: Frédéric Bonnaffous

Château Belgrave 33112 Saint-Laurent Médoc
GPS: Latitude: 45.151545 - Longitude: -0.780239
Tel. +33 (0)5 56 35 53 00 - Fax +33 (0)5 56 35 53 29
contact@dourthe.com - www.chateau-belgrave.com

# CHÂTEAU DE CAMENSAC
## GRAND CRU CLASSÉ EN 1855

*Owners: Jean Merlaut and Céline Villars-Foubet*

Château de Camensac is located on the perimeter of the Médoc's great growths, bordering on the Saint-Julien appellation. The 75-hectare vineyard consists of Cabernet Sauvignon and Merlot vines on slopes with deep gravel soil over a mix of clay and hardpan.

It is a very old estate that was cited on Belleyme's famous 18th century map. Camensac means "on the water's way", and comes from the words *camens*, which means "path" or "way" and *ac*, which means "water" in local dialect. In the 17th century, monks dug ditches along the bottom of the gravelly rises. These contributed to the quality of the terroir by draining excess rainwater.

The Merlaut family acquired Camensac in time for the 2005 vintage. Céline Villars and Jean Merlaut are now in charge of the estate. The niece and uncle are also the respective owners of Chasse-Spleen and Gruaud-Larose. Éric Boissenot is the consulting oenologist. Cabernet Sauvignon now plays a greater role at Camensac. This variety is ideally suited to the deep gravel soil, producing wines with depth, fruit, elegance, and minerality. The old Merlot vines are totally complementary, yielding wines that add volume and body to the final blend.

| | |
|---|---|
| Area under vine | 75 hectares |
| Production | 250,000 bottles |
| Soil | Gravel, clay-sand-gravel and sand-gravel soil |
| Grape varieties | 60% Cabernet Sauvignon, 40% Merlot |
| Barrel ageing | 15-18 months - New barrels: 40% |
| Second wine | La Closerie de Camensac |

Office tours: Marion Castel - Group tours: Jennifer Pomiès

**Château de Camensac** Route de Saint-Julien - 33112 Saint-Laurent-Médoc
GPS: Latitude: 45.1467056 - Longitude: -0.7858322
Tel. +33 (0)5 56 59 41 69 - Fax +33 (0)5 56 59 41 73
info@chateaucamensac.com

# CHÂTEAU CANTEMERLE
## GRAND CRU CLASSÉ EN 1855

*Owner: Groupe SMA*

Located in the communes of Macau and Ludon, Château Cantemerle, designated a great growth in the famous 1855 classification, has deep fine gravel soil. Thanks to its unique terroir, Cantemerle produces complex, well-balanced, and refined wines.

After belonging to the Villeneuve (1576-1892) and Dubos (1892-1980) families, the château was acquired in 1981 by the SMABTP, a large mutual insurance company in the construction and civil engineering sector. The estate's long history is reflected in the château's distinctive architecture and the magnificent grounds that surround it. Cantemerle exudes romantic charm and the vineyard has a magical feel to it.

Attractive even when quite young, the wine is rich, powerful, and smooth. It is made by an experienced and enthusiastic team using a careful blend of traditional and state-of-the-art techniques.

| | |
|---|---|
| Area under vine | 91 hectares |
| Production | 400,000 bottles |
| Soil | Siliceous and deep gravel from the Quaternary Period |
| Grape varieties | 60% Cabernet Sauvignon, 30% Merlot, 6% Cabernet franc, 4% Petit Verdot |
| Barrel ageing | 12-14 months - New barrels: 40% |
| Second wine | Allées de Cantemerle |

Managing Director: Philippe Dambrine

Château Cantemerle 33460 Macau
GPS: Latitude: 44.9931576 - Longitude: -0.6241741
Tel. +33 (0)5 57 97 02 82 - Fax +33 (0)5 57 97 02 84
cantemerle@cantemerle.com - **www.cantemerle.com**

99

# CHÂTEAU CITRAN

Owner: the Merlaut family

Château Citran is one of the oldest estates in the Médoc. The Donissan de Citran family reigned over this former Médoc seigneury from the 13th century until 1832. The present-day château was rebuilt between 1862 and 1864 on the site of the original medieval castle. Château Citran was propelled it to the forefront of Médoc wines in the late 19th century thanks to Monsieur Clauzel, a rich businessman responsible for giving the estate its present form. Set in beautiful grounds and surrounded by a moat, Château Citran is a listed historic monument.

In 1996, the Merlaut family, already deeply involved in the Bordeaux wine industry, took over the beautiful estate. Today, Citran has over 100 hectares of vines in the Haut-Médoc appellation. These are planted with premium grape varieties that make the most of its fine terroir: Cabernet Sauvignon, Merlot, and Cabernet Franc.

A healthy balance between traditional and modern techniques prevails in both the vineyard and cellars to produce a very elegant and distinguished wine. Château Citran's emblem is a peacock, such as the ones that can be seen roaming around the grounds. The wine is known around the world for its quality and finesse.

100

| | |
|---|---|
| Area under vine | 100 hectares |
| Production | 300,000 bottles |
| Soil | Gravel and sand on asteriated limestone and clay-limestone soil |
| Grape varieties | 50% Merlot, 45% Cabernet Sauvignon, 5% Cabernet franc |
| Barrel ageing | 15-18 months - New barrels: 35% |
| Second wine | Moulins de Citran |

Château Citran Chemin de Citran - 33480 Avensan
GPS: Latitude: 45.0491048 - Longitude: -0.7489337
Tel. +33 (0)5 56 58 21 01 - Fax +33 (0)5 57 88 84 60
info@citran.com - www.citran.com

# Château Coufran

*Owner: the Miailhe family*

Château Coufran was acquired in 1924 by Louis Miailhe, the grandfather of the present owners. The Miailhe family were well-known wine brokers at the time, with experience in the profession going back to 1793. As time went on, they came to own a number of well-known Médoc wine châteaux. Jean Miailhe's children, Marie-Cécile Vicaire and Éric Miailhe, now manage the family estates: Château Coufran and Château Verdignan.

Often called the "Pomerol of the Médoc" because it is made nearly entirely from Merlot, Château Coufran has a fine location overlooking the Gironde estuary, with a mild microclimate and fine sun exposure.

This large estate produces in excess of 400,000 bottles of generous, concentrated wine that ages very well. Furthermore, Château Coufran specialises in selling wines that are ready to drink. Modern storage facilities house large quantities of wines from the previous ten years. This makes it possible to appreciate mature wines with an excellent quality/price ratio, and whose provenance one can be assured of.

| | |
|---|---|
| Area under vine | 76 hectares |
| Production | 420,000 bottles |
| Soil | Garonne gravel |
| Grape varieties | 85% Merlot, 15% Cabernet Sauvignon |
| Barrel ageing | 12-18 months - New barrels: 25% |
| Second wine | N°2 de Coufran |

Château Coufran 33180 Saint-Seurin-de-Cadourne
GPS: Latitude: 45.302437 - Longitude: -0.788913
Tel. Château +33 (0)5 56 59 31 02 - Bureau +33 (0)5 56 44 90 84 - Fax +33 (0)5 56 81 32 35
contact@chateau-coufran.com - **www.chateau-coufran.com**

101

# CHÂTEAU LA LAGUNE
## GRAND CRU CLASSÉ EN 1855

Château La Lagune is located on a terrace of alluvial gravel parallel to the palus (rich soil that is productive, but not for quality wine) bordering the river. The "Village de La Lagune" was built here in 1525. Circa 1587, a certain Monsieur Eyral built a tenant farm in its place and gradually invested in transforming several modest leaseholds into a major winegrowing estate.

He was succeeded by numerous owners and the lovely château we know today was built between 1730 and 1734. In 1855, La Lagune joined the select club of grands crus classés as a third growth. The Sèze family acquired La Lagune in 1886 and it stayed with them until 1956. They sold to Georges Brunet, who gave an important new impetus to the estate before in turn selling it to the family who owned Champagne Ayala in 1964.

The Frey family arrived in 2000. They have made large-scale investments in the vineyard, cellars, and château aiming for excellence at all levels.

| | |
|---|---|
| Area under vine | 82 hectares |
| Production | 150,000 bottles |
| Soil | Gravel |
| Grape varieties | 60% Cabernet Sauvignon, 30% Merlot, 10% Petit Verdot |
| Barrel ageing | 18 months - New barrels: 50% |
| Second wine | Moulin de La Lagune |

Manager and oenologist: Caroline Frey

Château La Lagune 33290 Ludon-Médoc
GPS: Latitude: 44.9774613 - Longitude: -0.6182981
Tel. +33 (0)5 57 88 82 77 - Fax +33 (0)5 57 88 82 70
contact@chateau-lalagune.com - **www.chateau-lalagune.com**

# CHÂTEAU DE LAMARQUE

*Owner: the Gromand d'Evry family*

The seigneury of Lamarque takes its name from la marche (meaning "the marches", reflecting its location on the border of the province of Guyenne). The fortified château was built to defend the Médoc against Vikings invading from the Gironde estuary and was also subject to fierce assaults by the English during the Hundred Years' War.

Thalésie de Lamarque, who owned the château in 1247, was a very charming, happy person who left her mark on the castle and its surrounding vineyard. In fact, her presence is part of the vineyard's soul and can still be felt on evenings when a strong wind blows over the castle battlements.

Her spirit continues to accompany the talented men and women who take care of this superb terroir, giving the wines of Lamarque their brilliance, freshness, sensuality, and long aftertaste. 763 years later, her ancestor, Thalésie d'Everlange, the granddaughter of Marie-Hélène et Pierre-Gilles, embodies the same value.

| | |
|---|---|
| Area under vine | 42 hectares |
| Production | 180,000 bottles |
| Soil | 85% Garonne gravel, 5% clay-limestone soil, 10% sand and iron hardpan |
| Grape varieties | 45% Cabernet Sauvignon, 45% Merlot, 10% Petit Verdot |
| Barrel ageing | 16-18 months - New barrels: 40% |
| Second wine | Donjon de Lamarque |

Director: Pierre-Gilles Gromand d'Evry - Manager: Marie-Hélène Gromand d'Evry

Château de Lamarque 28, rue Principale - 33460 Lamarque
GPS: Latitude: 45.096061 - Longitude: -0.717636
Tel. +33 (0)5 56 58 90 03 - Fax +33 (0)5 56 58 93 43
lamarque@chateaudelamarque.fr - **www.chateaudelamarque.fr**

103

# CHÂTEAU LA TOUR CARNET
## GRAND CRU CLASSÉ EN 1855

## HAUT-MÉDOC

*Owner: Bernard Magrez*

Dating from the 12th century, La Tour Carnet is a genuine medieval castle with a moat. The oldest château in the Médoc, it owes its name to the equerry Carnet, who fought valiantly beside Lord Jean de Foy. Carnet's courage and devotion were such that he ended up inheriting the estate. Éléonore, the sister of Michel de Montaigne, was one of several illustrious owners during the 16th century.

The current owner, Bernard Magrez, has expended an enormous amount of time and energy in renovating the estate. His efforts have concerned the vineyard, the cellars, and the château.

Care is taken during pruning, leaf thinning, and green harvesting to reduce yields in the interest of quality. The grapes are hand picked into small crates and sorted by hand before being transferred by gravity flow into wooden fermentation vats and then into barrel. These are just a few of the practices that contribute to the excellence of this estate that was included in the prestigious 1855 classification.

104

| | |
|---|---|
| Area under vine | 122 hectares |
| Production | 400,000 bottles |
| Soil | Slopes facing south by southwest with gravel from the Günz glaciation period on a clay and limestone platform |
| Grape varieties | 59% Merlot, 37% Cabernet Sauvignon, 3% Petit Verdot, 1% Cabernet franc |
| Barrel ageing | 18 months - New barrels: 40% |
| Second wine | Les Douves de La Tour Carnet |

Supervisor of Bordeaux vineyards: Frédéric Chabaneau - Technical Director: Alix Combes

Château La Tour Carnet Route de Beychevelle - 33112 Saint-Laurent-Médoc
GPS: Latitude: 45.1472778 - Longitude: -0,7937662
Tel. +33 (0)5 56 73 30 90 - Fax +33 (0)5 56 59 48 54
latour@latour-carnet.com - **www.latour-carnet.com**

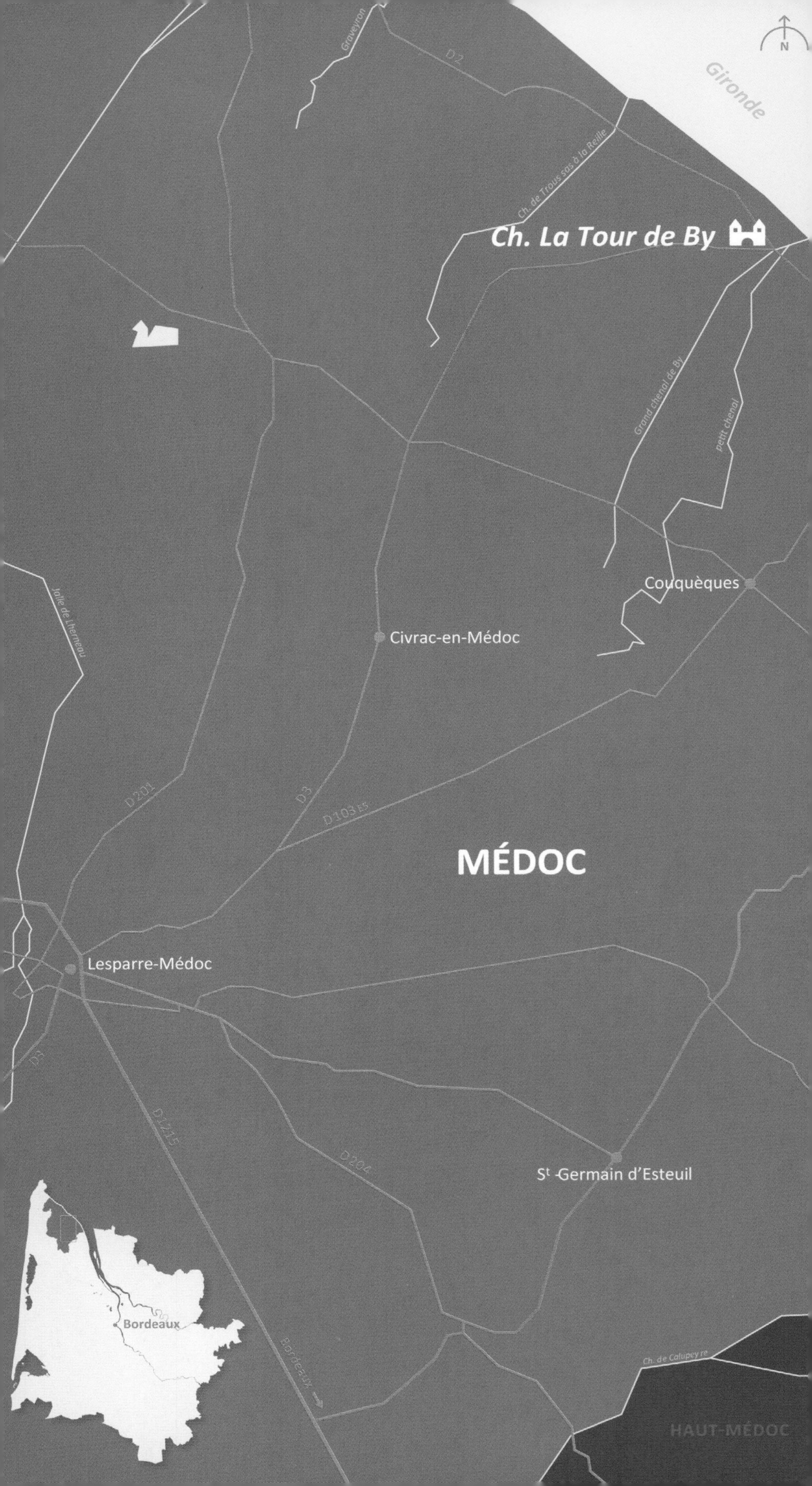

N

Gironde

Ch. de Trois sos à la Rolle

**Ch. La Tour de By** 🏰

Grand chenal de by

petit chenal

Couquèques

Joile de l'hermeau

Civrac-en-Médoc

D 2

Graveyron

D 201

D 3

D 103 is

**MÉDOC**

Lesparre-Médoc

D 3

D 1215

D 204

St -Germain d'Esteuil

Bordeaux

Bordeaux →

Ch. de Calupey re

HAUT-MÉDOC

# CRU DE MÉDOC

The Médoc is a huge triangular peninsula starting northwest of the city of Bordeaux, at a stream called the Jalle de Blanquefort, and going as far north as the Pointe de Grave. It is bordered by the Atlantic Ocean on the west and the Gironde estuary on the east. Located off the northern tip of this peninsula, Cordouan, "the King of Lighthouses", reflects the long history of the Bordeaux wine trade and the necessity for merchant ships to have safe access up and down the Gironde estuary.

Wine from the Médoc appellation comes mainly from vineyards located in the northern part of the peninsula, bordering the estuary, on a strip of land two to five km. wide, and 20 km. long, starting from Ordonnac in the south and going as far north as Vensac. The western boundary is limited at the drainage divide by a pine forest which serves as a natural windbreak against ocean gales.

p 108 | Château La Tour de By

# CHÂTEAU LA TOUR DE BY

**MÉDOC** — *Owners: Frédéric Le Clerc - Benjamin Richer de Forges*

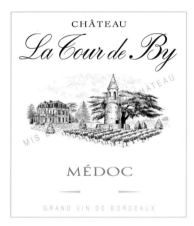

Vines have been grown at La Tour de By since the 16th century, and records show that the château was acquired by Pierre Tizon, lord of the fiefdom of By, in 1599. The tour, or tower, symbolising the estate is a former lighthouse built in the middle of the vines in 1825 to guide sailors navigating the Gironde estuary on foggy nights.

Marc Pagès, an agricultural engineer from Tunisia, purchased this beautiful estate in the northern Médoc in 1965 and was responsible for its rebirth. He was assisted by advice from Professor Émile Peynaud, who contributed enormously to making the most of the remarkable terroir.

Marc Pagès was one of the first French soldiers to participate in the liberation of Strasbourg alongside General Leclerc, in the second armoured division. He unquestionably brought Château La Tour de By up to its full potential in the four decades during which he managed it.

Frédéric Le Clerc continues his grandfather's efforts according to a philosophy combining quality, precision winemaking, and respect for tradition.

108

| | |
|---|---|
| Area under vine | 110 hectares |
| Production | 480,000 bottles |
| Soil | Gravel with iron hardpan subsoil |
| Grape varieties | 60% Cabernet Sauvignon, 35% Merlot, 5% Petit Verdot |
| Barrel ageing | 12 months - New barrels: 30% |
| Second wine | La Roque de By |

Manager: Frédéric Le Clerc - Commercial Director: Benjamin Richer de Forges

Château La Tour de By 5 rue de la Tour de By - 33340 Bégadan
GPS: Latitude: 45.3770901 - Longitude: -0.8511275
Tel. +33 (0)5 56 41 50 03 - Fax +33 (0)5 56 41 36 10
info@latourdeby.fr - **boutique.la-tour-de-by.com**

# MARGAUX

la Gironde

Île Macau

Île Margaux

Île Cazeau

N

Ch. Labégorce

Ch. Ferrière

Ch. Malescot
Saint-Exupery

Margaux

Ch. Durfort-Vivens

Ch.
Lascombes

Ch. Marquis de Terme

Ch. Rauzan-Gassies

Ch. Rauzan-Ségla

Ch. Prieuré-Lichine

Cantenac

Ch. Desmirail

La Maqueline

D2

Ch. Cantenac-
Brown

Ch. Kirwan

Ch. Brane-
Cantenac

Labarde

Lourina

Ch. Siran

Ch. Dauza

Parise

Ch. Angludet

Le Moulinot

Ch. Giscours

D 105 E1

Ch. du Tertre

Av. J-L Vonderheyden

Ch. Monbrison

Arsac

D 208

HAUT-MÉDOC

Bordeaux

Fond de Martian

La Mouline

Lesclause

Bordeaux

The name Margaux is magical and reflects a history of winemaking going back a thousand years. As with most vineyard areas close to the city of Bordeaux, wine production began during the Gallo-Roman period.

Records from the early 18th century refer to numerous winegrowing estates. While the château whose name is eponymous with the appellation already had a long history of selling their wines, it was only in the late 18th century that other vineyard owners became aware of the value of their land and introduced the production and ageing methods that gave rise to the grands crus of Margaux.

It took more than a century after the famous classification of 1855 for this large, complex region to put conflicts between communes behind it and for the rigorously delimited Margaux appellation to be recognized.

# CHÂTEAU ANGLUDET

*Owner: the Sichel family*

Château Angludet belongs to the Sichel family, Bordeaux wine merchants for six generations. It is one of the oldest estates in the Médoc. Records going back to the year 1150 mention a "noble residence" in Angludet, a name which means "Angle of High Land". The first lord of the manor, referred to in a deed dated 1273, was the knight Bertrand d'Angludet. The vineyard has had practically the same configuration since 1758 – thus for over 250 years – which is exceedingly rare.

Diana and Peter Sichel fell in love with Angludet and acquired it in 1961. They undertook a major renovation and Peter Sichel made constant improvements during the 40 years he was in charge. It is now one of the finest wines in Margaux. After Peter Sichel's death in 1998, his wife, Diana, and their six children have continued his efforts to make the best possible wine.

Since 1989, Benjamin Sichel manages the estate and oversees all aspects of viticulture and winemaking. He is also attentive to using natural, sustainable practices in the vineyard.

112

| | |
|---|---|
| Area under vine | 30 hectares |
| Production | 100,000 bottles |
| Soil | Gravel |
| Grape varieties | 46% Cabernet Sauvignon, 41% Merlot, 13% Petit Verdot |
| Barrel ageing | 18 months - New barrels: 35% |
| Second wine | Réserve d'Angludet |

Gérant : Benjamin Sichel

Château Angludet 33460 Cantenac
GPS: Latitude: 45.014946 - Longitude: -0.66168
Tel. +33 (0)5 57 88 71 41 - Fax. +33 (0)5 57 88 72 52
contact@chateau-angludet.fr - **www.chateau-angludet.fr**

# CHÂTEAU BRANE-CANTENAC

## GRAND CRU CLASSÉ EN 1855

*Owner: Henri Lurton*

Founded in the 18th century (when it was known as "Gorce") and considered one of the best second growths at the time of the 1855 Médoc classification, this estate is located on one of the finest gravelly hillocks in Cantenac. Indeed, Brane-Cantenac was often sold at first growth prices!

The estate was acquired in 1833 by Baron de Brane, known as "Napoleon of the Vines," who renamed it Brane-Cantenac. In 1925, Léonce Récapet, owner of Château Margaux, purchased the property. His grandson, Lucien Lurton, took over the reins in 1956. In 1992, Lucien's son Henri, oenologist and ampelographer, followed in his father's footsteps after having gained experience in South Africa and Chile.

From the moment he arrived, Henri Lurton has done his utmost to make this great Margaux reflect the brilliance and complexity of its outstanding terroir year in and year out, always seeking a balance between vintage character and the wine's intrinsic elegance. Brane-Cantenac now has a state-of-the-art cellar with sophisticated equipment such as a new optical sorting system, and its owner is totally dedicated to producing the best possible wines!

| | |
|---|---|
| Area under vine | 75 hectares |
| Production | 150,000 bottles |
| Soil | Deep gravel from the Quaternary Period |
| Grape varieties | 55% Cabernet Sauvignon, 40% Merlot, 4.5% Cabernet franc, 0.5% Carmenère |
| Barrel ageing | 18 months - New barrels: 60-70% |
| Second wine | Baron de Brane |

Estate Manager: Christophe Capdeville - Commercial Director: Marie-Hélène Dussech
Vineyard Manager: Pierre Auché - Cellar Master: Florent Cillero

Château Brane-Cantenac 33460 Cantenac
GPS: Latitude: 45.02222 - Longitude: -0.67389
Tel. +33 (0)5 57 88 83 33 - Fax +33 (0)5 57 88 72 51
contact@brane-cantenac.com - **www.brane-cantenac.com**

# CHÂTEAU CANTENAC BROWN

## GRAND CRU CLASSÉ EN 1855

*Owner: the Simon Halabi family*

GRAND CRU CLASSÉ 1855

**CHÂTEAU**
**CANTENAC BROWN**

2010

**MARGAUX**

John-Lewis Brown acquired this estate in the early 19th century and decided to build a Tudor-style château there, reminiscent of his Scottish origins. This building, one of the most unusual in the Médoc, is surrounded by a remarkable English-style grounds.

John-Lewis Brown, a famous animal painter and lover of fine wine, organised sumptuous receptions at Château Cantenac-Brown until 1843, when the estate was sold to a banker, Mr. Gromard.

The quality of the wine was acknowledged in the 1855 classification, when Château Cantenac-Brown was included among the third growths.

One hundred fifty years later, the Simon Halabi family has given a new impetus to this estate with a British atmosphere, which they are determined to raise to the very highest level. José Sanfins presently manages Cantenac Brown. He does his utmost to make the most of the magnificent terroir, lavishing the greatest of care on the soil and the vines, with great respect for the environment. This meticulous attention to detail continues into the cellar, where everything possible is done to produce an exceptional wine.

114

| | |
|---|---|
| Area under vine | 48 hectares |
| Production | 130,000 bottles |
| Soil | Garonne Gravel |
| Grape varieties | 65% Cabernet Sauvignon, 30% Merlot, 5% Cabernet franc |
| Barrel ageing | 15 months - New barrels: 60% |
| Second wine | BriO de Cantenac Brown |

Managing Director and Winemaker: José Sanfins

Château Cantenac Brown 33460 Cantenac
GPS: Latitude: 45.0208177 - Longitude: -0.6793229
Tel. +33 (0)5 57 88 81 81 - Fax +33 (0)5 57 88 81 90
contact@cantenacbrown.com - **www.cantenacbrown.com**

# CHÂTEAU DAUZAC
## GRAND CRU CLASSÉ EN 1855

Château Dauzac has inherited a long tradition of innovation. The estate's history is full of visionaries with new ideas that have enabled Dauzac's outstanding terroir to come through in the wine.

1685: wine merchant Paul Drouillard transforms Dauzac into one of the finest wine estates in the Médoc

1855: the Wiebroock family, who had acquired the estate in 1841, obtain recognition of Château Dauzac in the famous classification.

1863: the Johnstons, also owners of Château Ducru-Beaucaillou, perfect the famous bouillie bordelaise (copper sulphate soution) at Dauza, thereby helping to save the European vineyards from destruction.

1929: Jean-Jacques Bernat acquires the estate. He was the first to practise temperature control during fermentation by using blocks of ice.

1988, the MAIF (or *Mutuelle d'Assurance des Instituteurs de France*) mutual insurance company acquires the estate.

2013: Dauzac's new Managing Director, Laurent Fortin, institutes a development plan to strengthen the estate's position and enhance the renaissance of this unique great growth.

| | |
|---|---|
| Area under vine | 45 hectares |
| Production | 110,000 bottles |
| Soil | Deep rises of gravel from the Quartenary Period |
| Grape varieties | 63% Cabernet Sauvignon, 37% Merlot |
| Barrel ageing | 16 months - New barrels: 70% |
| Second wine | Aurore de Dauzac |

Managing Director: Laurent Fortin - Technical Director: Philippe Roux

Château Dauzac 1 avenue Georges Johnston - 33460 Labarde
GPS: Latitude: 45.0188395 - Longitude: -0.624448
Tel. +33 (0)5 57 88 32 10 - Tours +33 (0)5 57 88 96 00
chateaudauzac@chateaudauzac.com - **www.chateaudauzac.com**

# CHÂTEAU DESMIRAIL
## GRAND CRU CLASSÉ EN 1855

Owner: Denis Lurton

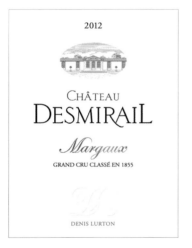

Château Desmirail, included among the third growths in the 1855 classification, has an outstanding terroir bordering on the Route des Châteaux. The elegant 18th century manor house is located behind a majestic gate made of pink marble. The cellar features a vat room typical of those from the late 19th century Médoc.

From these buildings full of history, visitors can admire the magnificent roof structure resembling the upside-down hull of a ship and the attractive vat-room with new wooden vats.

Jean Desmirail gave his name to the château after marrying an heiress from the Rausan family in the late 17th century.

The current owner and manager, Denis Lurton, took over from his father, Lucien, in 1992. He has invested in modernising the estate on a regular basis ever since. Château Desmirail produces smooth, elegant wines in the classic Margaux style.

116

| | |
|---|---|
| Area under vine | 37 hectares |
| Production | 100,000 bottles |
| Soil | Deep gravel from the Quaternary Period |
| Grape varieties | 60% Cabernet Sauvignon, 37% Merlot, 3% Petit Verdot |
| Barrel ageing | 14 months - New barrels: 40% |
| Second wine | Initial de Desmirail |

**Château Desmirail** 28 avenue de la Vᵉ République - 33460 Cantenac
GPS: Latitude: 45.028627 - Longitude: -0.654245
Tel. +33 (0)5 57 88 34 33 - Fax +33 (0)5 57 88 96 27
contact@desmirail.com - **www.desmirail.com**

# CHÂTEAU DURFORT-VIVENS

### GRAND CRU CLASSÉ EN 1855

*Owner: Gonzague Lurton*

Founded in the 14th century by the Durfort de Duras family, the estate stayed in their hands until the 19th century. In 1824, Viscount de Vivens added his name to that of Durfort. Already a famous wine by the time Thomas Jefferson cited it in the late 18th century, the estate was included among the first of the second growths in the famous 1855 classification. Lucien Lurton acquired Durfort-Vivens in 1961. His son, Gonzague, presently manages the estate.

His excellent understanding of the terroir and ecologically-responsible winegrowing practices are conducive to growing perfectly ripe grapes that produce wines of character.

The environmentally-friendly facilities and techniques used at Durfort-Vivens result in the optimum expression of grapes from each separate plot. Furthermore, the different-size oak and cement fermentation vats are adapted to the yields of every plot. The wine is aged in cellars that have an ideal natural temperature and humidity.

A superb terroir, state-of-the-art technology, and respect for the environment make Château Durfort-Vivens a truly unique wine.

| | |
|---|---|
| Area under vine | 55 hectares |
| Production | 150,000 bottles |
| Soil | Gravel from the Quaternary Period |
| Grape varieties | 70% Cabernet Sauvignon, 25% Merlot, 5% Cabernet franc |
| Barrel ageing | 18 months - New barrels: 50% |
| Second wine | Vivens / Relais de Durfort-Vivens |

Director: Jérôme Heranval - Technical Director: Léopold Valentin

Château Durfort-Vivens 3 rue du Général de Gaulle - 33460 Margaux
GPS: Latitude: 45.039863 - Longitude: -0.675421
Tel. +33 (0)5 57 88 31 02 - Fax +33 (0)5 57 88 60 60
infos@durfort-vivens.com - **www.durfort-vivens.com**

# CHÂTEAU FERRIÈRE
## GRAND CRU CLASSÉ EN 1855

*Owner: Claire Villars Lurton*

Gabriel Ferrière was the founder of the estate and he was a member of the royal court in the XVIIIth century. In 1855, Château Ferrière was classified third Growth. In 1988, the Villars-Merlaut family bought Ferrière from Alexis Lichine (also owner of Château Lascombes) and took over winemaking there in 1992 when the previous lease came to an end.

With its 18 hectares, mainly located on the land of Margaux and its terroir made of deep gravels from the Garonne River, Château Ferrière is one of the smallest of the Classified Growths in 1855.

The size of the vineyard, combined with a beautiful terroir, make Château Ferrière a rare and much sought-after wine.

Claire Villars Lurton is the owner of this estate and has undertaken an in-depth renovation of the winemaking facilities, as well as gradually converting to biodynamic viticulture. Ferrière is certified organic in 2015. With the greatest of care and attention, Claire Villars Lurton does her utmost to reflect Château Ferrière's outstanding terroir in her wine.

118

| | |
|---|---|
| Area under vine | 18 hectares |
| Production | 60,000 bottles |
| Soil | Deep gravel on limestone marl |
| Grape varieties | 61% Cabernet Sauvignon, 31% Merlot, 6% Petit Verdot, 2% Cabernet franc |
| Barrel ageing | 18 months - New barrels: 40% |
| Second wine | Les Remparts de Ferrière |

Château Ferrière 33 bis rue de la Trémoille - 33460 Margaux
GPS: Latitude: 45.0435599 - Longitude: -0.677651
Tel. +33 (0)5 57 88 76 65 - Fax +33 (0)5 57 88 98 33
infos@ferriere.com - **www.ferriere.com**

# CHÂTEAU GISCOURS
## GRAND CRU CLASSÉ EN 1855

## MARGAUX

The history of Château Giscours goes back to the 14th century, at which time an impressive keep protected the estate from potential attacks. However, the true creation of the estate can be considered to date from the purchase of the "maison noble de Guyscoutz" by Pierre de Lhomme, a rich cloth merchant, in 1552. This marked the beginning of Château Giscours' winegrowing tradition.

The estate underwent a golden age in the 19th century thanks to wealthy and influential owners such as the Promis, Pescatore, and Cruse families. This is also when Giscours underwent a number of important changes: the château was transformed into a neoclassic palace, the grounds were landscaped by Eugène Bülher, rare tree species were planted, and immense outbuildings were built, including the famous Ferme Suzanne...

In 1995, a Dutch businessman, Éric Albada Jelgersma, took over management and set about meticulously renovating the vineyard and buildings to make this prestigious estate fully worthy of its third growth ranking in the 1855 classification.

| | |
|---|---|
| Area under vine | 90 hectares |
| Production | 280,000 bottles |
| Soil | Deep Garonne gravel |
| Grape varieties | 60% Cabernet Sauvignon, 32% Merlot, 5% Cabernet franc, 3% Petit Verdot |
| Barrel ageing | 15-17 months - New barrels: 50% |
| Second wine | La Sirène de Giscours |

Chief Executive Officer: Éric Albada Jelgersma - Managing Director: Alexander Van Beek
Technical Director: Didier Forêt

Château Giscours 10 route de Giscours - 33460 Labarde
GPS: Latitude: 45.0084998 - Longitude: -0.6454524
Tel. +33 (0)5 57 97 09 09 - Fax +33 (0)5 57 97 09 00
giscours@chateau-giscours.fr - **www.chateau-giscours.fr**

# CHÂTEAU KIRWAN
## GRAND CRU CLASSÉ EN 1855

| MARGAUX | *Owner: the Schÿler family* |

Kirwan is an infinitely charming estate. The late 18th century château was built by Mark Kirwan, a prosperous Irish businessman who combined two small adjoining vineyards in the village of Cantenac and gave his name to the new entity. He did much to enhance the wine's reputation, and the book "Thomas Jefferson on Wine" tells us that the third American president praised the wine greatly during a trip to Bordeaux in 1787, noting that "Château de Quirouen" was in the 2nd category, along with "Ségur", "Lynch", etc.

Château Kirwan was listed as the first of the third growths in 1855, when a classification of Médoc wines was made for the universal exhibition during the reign of Napoleon III. The Godard family acquired Kirwan in the latter half of the 19th century. They expanded the vineyards and designed beautiful grounds and gardens with a fish pond and rose arbour.

The Schÿler family purchased Kirwan in 1926. Originating from cities belonging to the Hanseatic League, the Schÿlers came to Bordeaux in 1739 to establish a wine business. They made major investments at Kirwan starting in the 1970s and are closely identified with this great wine. In 2007, Sophie, Nathalie and Yann Schÿler's expertise was complemented by the appointment of a new managing director, the experienced oenologist Philippe Delfaut.

| | |
|---|---|
| Area under vine | 37 hectares |
| Production | 90,000 bottles |
| Soil | Pyrenean gravel on the Cantenac plateau and sand and gravel on the clay subsoil |
| Grape varieties | 45% Cabernet Sauvignon, 30% Merlot, 15% Cabernet franc, 10% Petit Verdot |
| Barrel ageing | 18-22 months - New barrels: 50% |
| Second wine | Charmes de Kirwan |

Managing Director: Philippe Delfaut
Marketing and Communication Director: Sophie Schÿler-Thierry
Tourism and Special Events Director: Nathalie Schÿler

Château Kirwan 33460 Cantenac
GPS: Latitude: 45.026633 - Longitude: -0.657622
Tel. +33 (0)5 57 88 71 00 - Fax +33 (0)5 57 88 77 62
mail@chateau-kirwan.com - **www.chateau-kirwan.com**

# CHÂTEAU LABÉGORCE

This elegant neoclassical château is located on the famous Route des Châteaux. Seventy hectares of the 250-hectare estate are devoted to viticulture. Bordering on châteaux Margaux and Lascombes, this property is mentioned in the 1868 edition of Cocks and Feret ("Bordeaux and its Wines"), which tells us of the existence since 1332 of "a vineyard belonging to the noble La Bégorce family". The château is described as "... one of the most beautiful and best situated in the town of Margaux".

The Perrodo family acquired Labégorce in 1989 and renovated not only the château building, but also the vineyard. They also improved winemaking, and Labégorce is now a charming wine with beautiful structure, bright fruit, and great finesse. The Perrodo family also acquired in 2006 Château Marquis d'Alesme, a third growth Margaux, which they aim to transform into one of the jewels of the appellation.

| | |
|---|---|
| Area under vine | 70 hectares |
| Production | 120-140,000 bottles |
| Soil | 70% sand and gravel, 30% sand and silt |
| Grape varieties | 50% Cabernet Sauvignon, 45% Merlot, 3% Cabernet franc, 2% Petit Verdot |
| Barrel ageing | 12-14 months - New barrels: 40-50% |
| Second wine | Zédé de Labégorce |

Owned by the Perrodo family, represented by Nathalie Perrodo-Samani
Managing Director: Marjolaine Maurice de Coninck - Commercial Director: Delphine Dariol Kolasa

Château Labégorce 1 route de Labégorce 33460 Margaux
GPS: Latitude: 45.05198 - Longitude: -0,688148
Tel. +33 (0)5 57 88 71 32 - Fax +33 (0)5 57 88 35 01
contact@labegorce.com - **www.chateau-labegorce.fr**

# CHÂTEAU LASCOMBES
## GRAND CRU CLASSÉ EN 1855

**MARGAUX**　　　　　　　　　　　　　　　　*Owner: MACSF*

With one hundred eighteen hectares of vines (including one hundred twelve in the Margaux appellation and six in the Haut-Médoc appellation) Château Lascombes is one of the largest estates in the Médoc. Included among the second growths in the 1855 classification, the estate has a prestigious history going back to Chevalier de Lascombes, born in 1625. The terroir consists of forty of the finest plots in the Margaux appellation.

The best traditional and modern techniques are used in the vineyard and cellar to produce powerful, concentrated, fruity, and elegant wine. The fact that the various plots are widely scattered gives Lascombes remarkable complexity, balance, and ageing potential.

A new era began in 2001 with the appointment of Dominique Befve as manager. Since then, the cellars and vineyard have been entirely restructured in order to produce wine worthy of Lascombes' classification and appellation.

The estate has been owned by the MACSF (Mutuelle d'Assurance du Corps de Santé Français) insurance company since 2011, and continues to be managed by Dominique Befve.

| | |
|---|---|
| Area under vine | 118 hectares |
| Production | 300,000 bottles |
| Soil | Clay-limestone, clay-gravel, and gravel |
| Grape varieties | 50% Merlot, 45% Cabernet Sauvignon, 5% Petit Verdot |
| Barrel ageing | 18 months - New barrels: 80-100% |
| Second wine | Chevalier de Lascombes |

President: Stéphane Dessirier - Managing Director: Dominique Befve - Consultant oenologist: Michel Rolland

Château Lascombes 1 cours de Verdun - 33460 Margaux
GPS: Latitude: 45.0402218 - Longitude: -0.6836185
Tel. +33 (0)5 57 88 70 66 - Fax +33 (0)5 57 88 72 17
visite.lascombes@chateau-lascombes.fr - **www.chateau-lascombes.com**

# CHÂTEAU MALESCOT ST-EXUPÉRY

### GRAND CRU CLASSÉ EN 1855

**MARGAUX**

*Owner: Jean-Luc Zuger*

Château Malescot St-Exupéry owes its name to two former owners: Simon Malescot, a royal councillor to the Bordeaux parliament, who acquired the estate in 1697, and Count Jean-Baptiste de Saint-Exupéry, who owned it from 1827 to 1853.

Paul Zuger and his son, Roger, purchased the château, located in the middle of the town of Margaux, in June 1955. After more than thirty years of unstinting efforts, Malescot St-Exupéry's coat of arms has never been truer: Semper Ad Altum ("Ever Higher"). The 45-hectare estate has 23.5 hectares of vines on a fine terroir that "overlooks the river" – indicative of the best vineyard sites according to an old local saying.

Connoisseurs very much appreciate the outstanding bouquet of this great growth, whose fruitiness and body go together beautifully with meat dishes and cheeses.

| | |
|---|---|
| Area under vine | 28 hectares |
| Production | 120,000 bottles |
| Soil | Pyrenean gravel |
| Grape varieties | 50% Cabernet Sauvignon, 35% Merlot, 10% Cabernet franc, 5% Petit Verdot |
| Barrel ageing | 12-14 months - New barrels: 100% |
| Second wine | Dame de Malescot |

Château Malescot St-Exupéry 33460 Margaux
GPS: Latitude: 45.0411142 - Longitude: -0.6761154
Tel. +33 (0)5 57 88 97 20 - Fax +33 (0)5 57 88 97 21
jeanluczuger@malescot.com - **www.malescot.com**

# CHÂTEAU MARQUIS DE TERME
## GRAND CRU CLASSÉ EN 1855

**MARGAUX**

*Owners: the Sénéclauze family*

GRAND VIN DE BORDEAUX

CHATEAU
**MARQUIS DE TERME**

2010

MARGAUX

GRAND CRU CLASSÉ EN 1855

In December 1762, Lord Péguilhan – otherwise known as the Marquis de Terme - received the estate as part of his wife's dowry and gave it his name.

The fame of Marquis de Terme dates back to Thomas Jefferson! Before being elected President of the United States, Jefferson visited Bordeaux in 1787 and listed Château Marquis de Terme as one of the sixteen best wines he had tasted. The château was also included among the great growths in the famous 1855 classification.

Successive generations have worked hard to ensure the development of the property that has belonged to the Sénéclauze family since 1935.

In 2009, the owners appointed Ludovic David as General Manager. He introduced a new approach to winemaking by implementing numerous technical, viticultural, and architectural innovations.

The vineyard is managed on a plot-by-plot basis with strong respect for the environment. The grapes are all picked by hand and meticulously sorted so that only the most beautiful berries make their way into the vats.

As a classified growth that is managed on a human scale Château Marquis de Terme displays the best of both traditional and modern winemaking methods.

| | |
|---|---|
| Area under vine | 39 hectares |
| Production | 130,000 bottles |
| Soil | Gravel typical of the Margaux appellation, with quartz and quartzite. Greater concentration of clay in the subsoil |
| Grape varieties | 60% Cabernet Sauvignon, 35% Merlot, 5% Petit Verdot |
| Barrel ageing | 16 months - New barrels: 50% |
| Second wine | La Couronne de Marquis de Terme |

Managing Director: Ludovic David

Château Marquis de Terme 3 route de Rauzan - 33460 Margaux
GPS: Latitude: 45.038394 - Longitude: -0.6773689999999988
Tel. +33 (0)5 57 88 30 01 - Fax +33 (0)5 57 88 32 51
mdt@chateau-marquis-de-terme.com - **www.chateau-marquis-de-terme.com**

# CHÂTEAU MONBRISON

**MARGAUX**

*Owner: Laurent Vonderheyden*

Château Monbrison has a very long history. It was created when half of a third classified growth in Margaux, was added to an existing vineyard as the result of an inheritance. The estate came into the hands of the eponymous Monsieur de Monbrison and was then acquired by Monsieur Chaix d'Est-Ange, a famous lawyer and President of the French Senate, who transformed it into a model vineyard.

Château Monbrison once again changed hands in 1887 when it was purchased by the négociant Jean Clanis. His family in turn sold Monbrison to Robert Meacham Davis in 1922, and the estate has since been managed by his children and grandchildren.

Laurent Vonderheyden has been in charge for the past twenty years, transforming Château Monbrison into one of the leading wines in its appellation. Well-received by critics, Monbrison has been awarded prestigious medals and distinctions in France and abroad. The quality of its enchanting bouquet is equalled only by the elegance it displays on the palate. Incredibly refined, Monbrison brilliantly reflects its superb terroir and is the epitome of a great Margaux.

| | |
|---|---|
| Area under vine | 13.20 hectares |
| Production | 48,000 bottles |
| Soil | Pyrenean gravel |
| Grape varieties | 69% Cabernet Sauvignon, 28% Merlot, 3% Petit Verdot |
| Barrel ageing | 18 months - New barrels: 40% |
| Second wine | Bouquet de Monbrison |

Château Monbrison 1 allée de Monbrison - 33460 Arsac
GPS: Latitude: 45.000243 - Longitude: -0.67628
Tel. +33 (0)5 56 58 80 04 - Fax +33 (0)5 56 58 85 33
lvdh33@wanadoo.fr - **www.chateaumonbrison.com**

# CHÂTEAU PRIEURÉ-LICHINE

## GRAND CRU CLASSÉ EN 1855

**MARGAUX**                                                   *Owner: Groupe Ballande*

2012

MARGAUX

APPELLATION MARGAUX CONTRÔLÉE

GRAND CRU CLASSÉ

MIS EN BOUTEILLE AU CHÂTEAU

Founded in the 12th century by monks from Vertheuil Abbey, the prieuré (or "priory") of Cantenac produced well-reputed wines from the very beginning. The vineyard belonged to the Church until the French Revolution.

In 1951, Alexis Lichine, called "the Pope of Wine", took over the estate and added his name two years later. Thanks to his patient determination, he was able to add new vineyard plots, modernize the cellars, and renovate the monks' former living quarters. Château Prieuré-Lichine's fate was linked to that of the Lichine family for nearly half a century.

Now owned by the Ballande group, the château has entered a dynamic new phase of its history with eight hectares of vines added in 2012, and brand new cellar.

A new approach to managing far-flung vineyard plots has turned this diversity into a decided advantage, enabling Prieuré-Lichine to express the full complexity of its terroir thanks to an experienced and devoted winemaking team.

| | |
|---|---|
| Area under vine | 78 hectares |
| Production | 192,000 bottles |
| Soil | Pyrenean gravel and gravel from the Günz glaciation period |
| Grape varieties | 55% Cabernet Sauvignon, 40% Merlot, 5% Petit Verdot |
| Barrel ageing | 18 months - New barrels: 50% |
| Second wine | Confidences de Prieuré-Lichine |

Managing Director: Stanislas Henriot - Sales and Communication: Lise Latrille
Technical Manager: Étienne Charrier

Château Prieuré-Lichine 34 avenue de la Vᵉ République - 33460 Cantenac
GPS: Latitude: 45.0286229 - Longitude: -0.6542153
Tel. +33 (0)5 57 88 36 28 - Fax +33 (0)5 57 88 78 93
contact@prieure-lichine.fr - **www.prieure-lichine.fr**

# CHÂTEAU RAUZAN-GASSIES
## GRAND CRU CLASSÉ EN 1855

MARGAUX                                    *Owner: the Quié family*

The origins of the noble house of Gassies in the Médoc go back to medieval times. The Lords of Gassies were considered knights, and owed allegiance to the owners of Château Margaux. Monsieur de Rauzan acquired the seigneury in 1661 and is responsible for establishing the reputation of its wine. The estate was divided into two parts in 1785. The name of one of these, Rauzan-Gassies, very much reflects its historic roots.

Since 1946, second growth Château Rauzan-Gassies has belonged to the Quié family, who also owns châteaux Croizet-Bages (a great growth of Pauillac) and Bel Orme Tronquoy de Lalande.

Monsieur Paul Quié undertook a major renovation of the vineyard during the postwar period. This was finalised by his son, Jean-Michel, who took over management in 1968. He is assisted by his children, Anne-Françoise and Jean-Philippe, in overseeing the three family châteaux.

Their passion for fine wine is very much in the tradition of the great growths of Bordeaux, and one of Jean-Michel Quié's greatest pleasures is to share his wine with people who are dear to him.

| | |
|---|---|
| Area under vine | 28.5 hectares |
| Production | 80,000 bottles |
| Soil | Deep gravel, gravel and sand |
| Grape varieties | 65% Cabernet Sauvignon, 25% Merlot, 5% Petit Verdot, 5% Cabernet franc |
| Barrel ageing | 12 months - New barrels: 50-55% |
| Second wine | Gassies |

Château Rauzan-Gassies 1 rue Alexis Millardet - 33460 Margaux
GPS: Latitude: 45.037393 - Longitude: -0.674975
Tel. +33 (0)5 57 88 71 88 - Fax +33 (0)5 57 88 37 49
rauzangassies@domaines-quie.com - **www.rauzangassies.fr**

**MARGAUX**

*Owner: Chanel*

Located a stone's throw from the village of Margaux, Château Rauzan-Ségla consists of a 70-hectare patchwork of vineyards reflecting the diversity of soils in the appellation, and forming a priceless treasure. Consisting primarily of alluvial gravel, the terroir is ideally suited to viticulture and features perfect drainage. It also reflects the best that each grape variety has to offer.

1661, Pierre Desmezures de Rauzan purchased an estate which he named after himself. The wine quickly acquired a fine reputation in France and abroad. This was confirmed in the famous 1855 classification, when the château was included among the second growths.

The estate was bought by Chanel in 1994, and work in the vineyards and cellars is done with the utmost care to produce a great and remarkably complex wine with fine ageing potential.

Vineyard workers at Rauzan-Ségla prune the vines, tie them up, pluck leaves, thin bunches, etc. to produce the best possible fruit. This is transformed into a powerful, long-lived wine with the greatest of care and attention.

| | |
|---|---|
| Area under vine | 70 hectares |
| Production | 110,000 bottles |
| Soil | Fine, deep gravel and clay |
| Grape varieties | 60% Cabernet Sauvignon, 37% Merlot, 1.5% Petit Verdot, 1.5% Cabernet franc |
| Barrel ageing | 18 months - New barrels: 60% |
| Second wine | Ségla |

Managing Director: Nicolas Audebert - Public Relations and Communication: Sandrine Bégaud

Château Rauzan-Ségla rue Alexis Millardet - BP 56 - 33460 Margaux
GPS: Latitude: 45.035716 - Longitude: -0.674715
Tel. +33 (0)5 57 88 82 10 - Fax +33 (0)5 57 88 34 54
contact@rauzan-segla.com - **www.chateaurauzansegla.com**

# CHÂTEAU SIRAN

Owner: S.C. Château Siran

Château Siran is located in Labarde, the southernmost commune in the Margaux appellation. Siran is undoubtedly one of the Médoc's great historic estates.

The 88-hectare property has 36 hectares of vines, of which 25 are in the Margaux appellation. The remarkable terroir consists of a plateau with siliceous gravel soil. Planted essentially with Cabernet Sauvignon and Merlot, this vineyard nevertheless has an unusually large percentage of Petit Verdot (13%) – a variety that contributes finesse, concentration and, above all, a spicy aftertaste typical of Château Siran. Siran is also one of the rare estates in Bordeaux to have belonged to the same family for over 150 years (the château was acquired in 1859 by the family who presently own it).

Representing the fifth generation, Édouard Miailhe has been at the helm of this unique estate since 2007. Helped by a new, young winemaking team, he is determined to perpetuate and enhance the château's fine reputation.

Château Siran produces from 120 to 150,000 bottles of their grand vin and second wine, S de Siran, every year.

| | |
|---|---|
| Area under vine | 25 hectares |
| Production | 80,000 bottles |
| Soil | Deep gravel |
| Grape varieties | 46% Merlot, 40% Cabernet Sauvignon, 13% Petit Verdot, 1% Cabernet franc |
| Barrel ageing | 12 months - New barrels: 35% |
| Second wine | S de Siran |

Co-Manager: Édouard Miailhe - Co-Manager: Brigitte Miailhe

Château Siran 13 avenue Comte JB de Lynch - 33460 Labarde
GPS: Latitude: 45.021667 - Longitude: -0.634444
Tel. +33 (0)5 57 88 34 04 - Fax +33 (0)5 57 88 70 05
info@chateausiran.com - www.chateausiran.com

129

# CHÂTEAU DU TERTRE
## GRAND CRU CLASSÉ EN 1855

MARGAUX                                          *Owner: Éric Albada Jelgersma*

Located on one of the highest and most beautiful gravelly rises in the Margaux appellation, Château du Tertre has a very interesting history. It was created in the 18th century by an important Irish négociant, Pierre Mitchell, who had fallen in love with the Bordeaux region and its wines. The founder of the first glassworks in Bordeaux, this refined, innovative man realized one of his fondest dreams by establishing his own fine wine estate.

Other famous families followed in his footsteps: the de Brezets and Vallandés, as well as the Koenigswarters, rich bankers close to Emperor Napoleon III. The quality of the wine was such that it was included among the great growths of Margaux in the 1855 classification.

Éric Albada Jelgersma acquired the estate in 1997. Thanks to major investments and careful management, Château du Tertre now expresses its intrinsically elegant personality year after year.

| | |
|---|---|
| Area under vine | 52 hectares |
| Production | 150,000 bottles |
| Soil | Günz gravel and sand |
| Grape varieties | 43% Cabernet Sauvignon, 33% Merlot, 19% Cabernet franc, 5% Petit Verdot |
| Barrel ageing | 15-17 months - New barrels: 45% |
| Second wine | Les Hauts du Tertre |

Managing Director: Alexander Van Beek - Technical Director: Frédéric Ardouin

Château du Tertre 33460 Arsac
GPS: Latitude: 45.02210 - Longitude: -0.405207
Tel. +33 (0)5 57 88 52 52 - Fax +33 (0)5 57 97 09 00
tertre@chateaudutertre.fr - **www.chateaudutertre.fr**

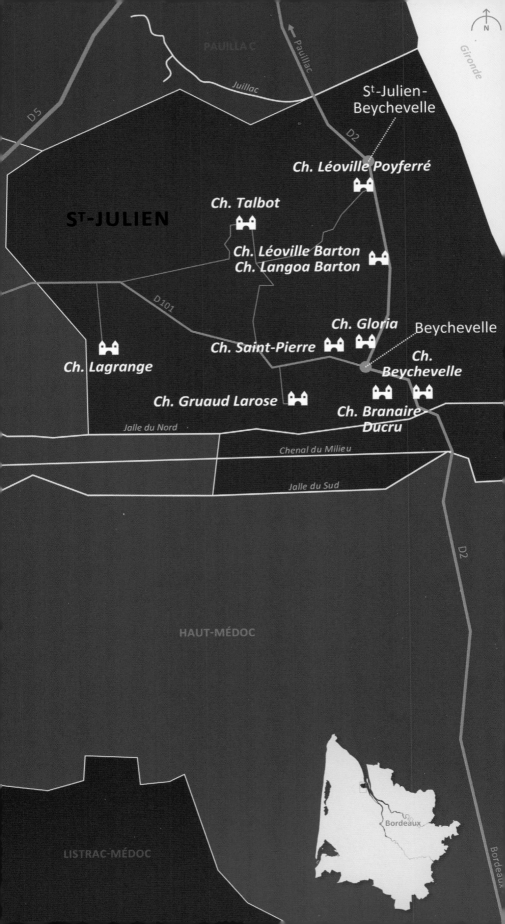

# CRUS DE SAINT-JULIEN

The parish of Saint-Julien dates back to the 7th century. Originally named Saint-Julien-de-Reignac, the town became known as Saint-Julien-Beychevelle in the early 20th century, combining the name of the small port and that of the hamlet famous for its fine wines.

Starting in the 17th century, aristocrats and other land owners made the most of the winegrowing potential of their outstanding terroir. They were responsible for creating the great estates included in the 1855 classification.

# CHÂTEAU BEYCHEVELLE

## GRAND CRU CLASSÉ EN 1855

## SAINT-JULIEN

*Owner: Grands millésimes de France*

**CHÂTEAU BEYCHEVELLE**
GRAND VIN 2009
— SAINT-JULIEN —

The spirit of this prestigious great growth was forged over three centuries.

During the reign of Henri III, Beychevelle was the fief of the Dukes of Épernon, including the first of that name, Jean-Louis Nogaret de La Valette, an admiral in the French navy. According to legend, ships passing in front of his château lowered their sails as a sign of allegiance to this powerful man. In fact, the name Beychevelle comes from the Old French Baisse-Voile, meaning "lowered sails", as reflected in the château's emblem. This depicts a ship with a griffin – the guardian of Dionysos' wine crater in Greek mythology – on the prow.

Built in the 17th century and reconstructed by Marquis de Brassier in 1757, "the Versailles of the Médoc" was restored to its original splendour in the late 20th century. The elegance of Beychevelle's architecture is reflected in its refined, well-balanced wine served at prestigious tables around the world.

The management is also very respectful of the environment, and the estate has been certified for sustainable viticulture.

134

| | |
|---|---|
| Area under vine | 78.8 hectares |
| Production | 240-260,000 bottles |
| Soil | Deep Garonne gravel |
| Grape varieties | 48% Cabernet Sauvignon, 43% Merlot, 6% Cabernet franc, 3% Petit Verdot |
| Barrel ageing | 16-18 months - New barrels: 50% |
| Second wine | Amiral de Beychevelle |

Manager: Aymar de Baillenx - Director: Philippe Blanc

Château Beychevelle 33250 Saint-Julien-Beychevelle
GPS: Latitude: 45.14497 - Longitude: -0.735079
Tel. +33 (0)5 56 73 20 70 - Fax +33 (0)5 56 73 20 71
beychevelle@beychevelle.com - **www.beychevelle.com**

# CHÂTEAU BRANAIRE-DUCRU
## GRAND CRU CLASSÉ EN 1855

**SAINT-JULIEN**

*Co-Owner: Patrick Maroteaux*

Jean-Baptiste Braneyre, the first person to own the estate in 1680, was well aware of the superb winegrowing potential of the gravelly soil located a stone's throw from the Gironde estuary. The 1855 classification was later to confirm the quality of our terroir. Branaire-Ducru and its prestigious neighbours form a group of châteaux that are famous the world over for their excellent wines.

In 1988, our family group asked me to write a new page in the history of this great growth. We defined the spirit in which we wanted to do this from the very first: to make quality an absolute priority and to do everything possible to express Branaire-Ducru's intrinsic personality and complexity.

Composed primarily of Cabernet Sauvignon, our wines express their character year in, year out with great regularity, displaying an enormous amount of fruit, freshness, and subtlety. The winemaking team is fully devoted to highlighting these characteristics in every vintage, and Branaire-Ducru is invariably an elegant wine and a quintessential Saint-Julien.

We are delighted whenever we think about the pleasure and emotions Branaire-Ducru provides to wine enthusiasts around the world.

| | |
|---|---|
| Area under vine | 60 hectares |
| Soil | Deep gravel from the Quaternary Period overlaying clay soil |
| Grape varieties | 70% Cabernet Sauvignon, 22% Merlot, 5% Cabernet franc, 3% Petit Verdot |
| Barrel ageing | 18 months - New barrels: 60% |
| Second wine | Duluc de Branaire-Ducru |

President: Patrick Maroteaux - Manager: François-Xavier Maroteaux - Manager: Jean-Dominique Videau

Château Branaire-Ducru 1 chemin du Bourdieu - 33250 Saint-Julien
GPS: Latitude: 45.144666 - Longitude: -0.739205
Tel. +33 (0)5 56 59 25 86 - Fax +33 (0)5 56 59 16 26
branaire@branaire.com - **www.branaire.com**

# CHÂTEAU GLORIA

Owner: S.C. Domaines Martin

Henri Martin creator of Château Gloria, was the grandson of the cellarmaster at Château Gruaud-Larose and son of a cooper in the village of Beychevelle. His family had been connected for many years with the vines and cellars that dot the Saint-Julien countryside. In fact, the Martins were variously vineyard workers, vineyard managers, and cellar workers for some three centuries. The dream of every vineyard worker in the Médoc is to buy a few rows of Cabernet or Merlot vines for the pleasure of cultivating their own land and to have something to leave to their children.

So, in the early 1940s, Henri Martin (who had started out a cooper like his father), turned his attention to viticulture. His first purchase was 6,000 vines in Saint-Julien alongside the family home in 1939. This was the beginning of what would later become Château Gloria, a patchwork of various plots scattered among classified growth vineyards. This was the work of his life.

Today, Françoise (his daughter) and Jean-Louis Triaud (his son-in-law), assisted by their children, Vanessa and Jean, continue the family tradition with passion.

136

| | |
|---|---|
| Area under vine | 50 hectares |
| Production | 250,000 bottles |
| Soil | Gravel from the Günz period on a clay-sand subsoil |
| Grape varieties | 65 % Cabernet Sauvignon, 25 % Merlot, 5 % Cabernet franc, 5 % Petit Verdot |
| Barrel ageing | 14 months - New barrels: 40 % |
| Second wine | Château Peymartin |

Joint Manager: Françoise Triaud – Joint Manager: Jean Triaud – Joint Manager: Vanessa Triaud

Château Gloria 33250 Saint-Julien-Beychevelle
GPS: Latitude: 45.1480185 - Longitude: -0.7418619
Tel. +33 (0)5 56 59 08 18 - Fax +33 (0)5 56 59 16 18
contact@domaines-martin.com - **www.domaines-henri-martin.com**

# CHÂTEAU GRUAUD LAROSE
## GRAND CRU CLASSÉ EN 1855

## SAINT-JULIEN

*Owner: Jean Merlaut*

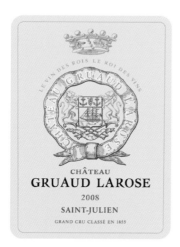

Gruaud Larose is named after the two people who created the estate. In 1725, Abbot Gruaud, bought 50 hectares of land and planted vines there. His nephew, Chevalier de Larose, inherited the property in 1781 and the vineyard grew to 80 hectares under his ownership. Seeing that there were no heirs, Gruaud Larose was jointly purchased by two families at auction in 1812. However, their relations soured and the vineyard was divided into two parts in 1865. In 1934, the Cordier family reunited the estate.

It has belonged to the Merlaut family since 1997. They have introduced sustainable development and organic farming methods in the vineyard. The terroir consists of slopes of deep Garonne gravel from the Quaternary Period (about 700,000 years ago) where Cabernet Sauvignon is king – as befits a wine whose motto is "The King of Wines and the Wine of Kings".

Château Gruaud Larose is one of the most historic estates in the Médoc. Its size has hardly changed through the centuries and today deserves its second growth status in the 1855 classification more than ever.

| | |
|---|---|
| Area under vine | 82 hectares |
| Production | 157,880 bottles |
| Soil | Garonne gravel from the Mindel I and Mindel II glaciations of the Quartenary Period |
| Grape varieties | 61% Cabernet Sauvignon, 29% Merlot, 7% Cabernet franc, 3% Petit Verdot |
| Barrel ageing | 18 months - New barrels: 80% |
| Second wine | Sarget de Gruaud |

Managing Director: Nicolas Sinoquet - Cellar Master: Stéphanie Lebaron - Vineyard Manager: Patrick Frédéric

**Château Gruaud Larose** chemin de Gruaud Larose - 33250 Saint-Julien-Beychevelle
GPS: Latitude: 44.147452 - Longitude: -0.74957
Tel. +33 (0)5 56 73 15 20 - Fax +33 (0)5 56 59 64 72
**www.gruaud-larose.com**

# CHÂTEAU LAGRANGE
## GRAND CRU CLASSÉ EN 1855

**SAINT-JULIEN**

*Owner: Suntory*

Château Lagrange's winegrowing vocation dates back to the 17th century. The estate was classified a third growth in 1855 thanks to the efforts and the vision of Count Dûchatel, who owned Lagrange from 1842 to 1874. He built a network of drains and extended the estate to 280 hectares, including 120 of vines. As Minister of the Interior during the reign of King Louis-Philippe and a member of the Academy of Fine Arts, he spread Lagrange's reputation far and wide.

In 1983, the Suntory group, the leading Japanese wine and spirits firm, acquired Lagrange and invested heavily in a spectacular renovation. Priority was given to the vineyard, followed by refurbishing and modernising the vat room and cellars. The efforts undertaken in the 1980s continue to the present day: work in the vineyard is done with great attention to detail and each plot is treated individually. The grapes are then fermented separately in order to fine tune and obtain the best possible final blend. The resulting wine is powerful, elegant, and the epitome of a great Saint-Julien.

A new management team, Matthieu Bordes and Keiichi Shiina, are in charge of this quest for perfection. In addition, production methods are more environmentally-friendly than ever.

138

| | |
|---|---|
| Area under vine | 118 hectares |
| Production | 300,000 bottles |
| Soil | Two Günz gravel rises |
| Grape varieties | 67% Cabernet Sauvignon, 28% Merlot, and 5% Petit Verdot |
| Barrel ageing | 18-20 months - New barrels: 60% |
| Second wine | Les Fiefs de Lagrange |

General Manager: Matthieu Bordes – Technical Director: Benjamin Vimal
Public Relations: Charlotte Denjean

Château Lagrange 33250 Saint-Julien-Beychevelle
GSP: Latitude: 45.149419 - Longitude: -0.773892
Tel. + 33 (0)5 56 73 38 38 - Fax +33 (0)5 56 59 26 09
chateau-lagrange@chateau-lagrange.com - **www.chateau-lagrange.com**

# CHÂTEAU LANGOA BARTON
## GRAND CRU CLASSÉ EN 1855

Château Langoa Barton was bought by Hugh Barton, an Irish, in 1821, more than 30 years before the classification of 1855 and Hugh was not to know that Langoa would be classified as a 3rd growth. It was surely the architecture and the beautiful façade built in 1758 that attracted him. Since then the property has remained in the family and today, Anthony Barton's daughter, Lilian Barton Sartorius manages the properties and the wine merchant company. Her two children Mélanie and Damien, both involved in the family history represent the 10th generation. The vineyards are situated at the south of the appellation Saint Julien and the style of the wine is described as typical Saint Julien. This means a wine of great elegance, charming and finesse with subtle flavors.

| | |
|---|---|
| Area under vine | 17 hectares |
| Production | 80,000 bottles |
| Soil | Gravel on clay |
| Grape varieties | 57% Cabernet Sauvignon, 34% Merlot, 9% Cabernet Franc |
| Barrel ageing | 18 months - New barrels: 60% |

President of the limited liability company: Lilian Barton-Sartorius - President of the Supervisory Council: Anthony Barton
Vice-President of the Supervisory Council: Eva Barton

Château Langoa Barton 33250 Saint-Julien-Beychevelle
GPS: Latitude: 45.157662 - Longitude: -0.738831
Tel. +33 (0)5 56 59 06 05 - Fax +33 (0)5 56 59 14 29
chateau@leoville-barton.com - **www.leoville-barton.com**

# Château Léoville Barton

### Grand Cru Classé en 1855

**Saint-Julien**

*Owner: the Barton family*

In 1826 Hugh Barton, an Irish already owner of Château Langoa Barton, purchased part of the vineyards of the big Léoville estate which then was renamed Château Léoville Barton. The property still belongs to the Barton family; it is classified as a second growth and is situated in the heart of the appellation Saint Julien. The current owners believe very much in the importance of "terroir" and consequently produce an authentic Saint Julien wine of great finesse and perfect balance avoiding the trend of excessive extraction and extreme alcohol. Twice in the history of the Bartons, one of the member has been obliged to flee from France: Hugh in 1793 during the French Revolution returned to Ireland after a short stay in prison in Bordeaux. Then Ronald Barton also had to abandon the property in 1940. He returned in 1945 to produce a mythical vintage. Today, Lilian Barton-Sartorius represents the 9th generation and the most ancient family still owner of their property since the classification of 1855.

| | |
|---|---|
| Area under vine | 51 hectares |
| Production | 200,000 bottles |
| Soil | Gravel on clay |
| Grape varieties | 74% Cabernet Sauvignon, 23% Merlot, 3% Cabernet franc |
| Barrel ageing | 18 months - New barrels: 60% |
| Second wine | La réserve de Léoville Barton |

President of the limited liability company: Lilian Barton-Sartorius - President of the Supervisory Council: Anthony Barton
Vice-President of the Supervisory Council: Eva Barton

Château Léoville Barton 33250 Saint-Julien-Beychevelle
GPS: Latitude: 45.157662 - Longitude: -0.738831
Tel. +33 (0)5 56 59 06 05 - Fax. +33 (0)5 56 59 14 29
chateau@leoville-barton.com - **www.leoville-barton.com**

# CHÂTEAU LÉOVILLE POYFERRÉ

### GRAND CRU CLASSÉ EN 1855

## SAINT-JULIEN

*Owner: the Cuvelier family*

Léoville Poyferré came into existence in 1840 as the result of a division of a larger estate, and was included among the second growths in the famous 1855 classification.

The Cuvelier family bought the estate in 1920 and Didier Cuvelier has been in charge of management since 1979.

He has made major investments, both in terms of equipment and human resources, ever since. The many improvements have always been in synergy with Léoville Poyferré's outstanding terroir, and all efforts are focused on faithfully reflecting this in the wine.

Constant care and attention, as well as innovation, have resulted in a very great wine that is distributed around the world.

Léoville Poyferré has perfect balance, great finesse, elegance, and remarkable ageing potential.

| | |
|---|---|
| Area under vine | 80 hectares |
| Production | 220,000 bottles |
| Soil | Garonne gravel |
| Grape varieties | 62.5% Cabernet Sauvignon, 25.5% Merlot, 6% Petit Verdot, 6% Cabernet franc |
| Barrel ageing | 18-20 months - New barrels: 80% |
| Second wine | Pavillon de Léoville Poyferré |

Manager: Didier Cuvelier

Château Léoville Poyferré 38 rue de Saint-Julien - 33250 Saint-Julien-Beychevelle
GPS: Latitude: 45.1640718 - Longitude: -0.7382187
Tel. +33 (0)5 56 59 08 30 - Fax +33 (0)5 56 59 60 09
lp@leoville-poyferre.fr - **www.leoville-poyferre.fr**

# CHÂTEAU SAINT-PIERRE
## GRAND CRU CLASSÉ EN 1855

## SAINT-JULIEN

*Owner: S.C. Domaines Martin*

Château Saint-Pierre's history dates back to the 16th century. Records from 1693 prove the existence of an estate named "Serançan" belonging to Marquis de Cheverry. Baron de Saint-Pierre bought the property in 1767, during the reign of Louis XV and, in keeping with the custom of the time, gave his name to it. His two daughters inherited the estate in 1832. Saint-Pierre was included among the fourth growths in the famous 1855 classification.

In 1892, Madame de Luetkens sold her share of the vineyard to Léon Sevaistre, after which Saint-Pierre was sold under two separate labels: Saint-Pierre-Sevaistre and Saint-Pierre-Bontemps-Dubarry.

In 1922, Belgian wine merchants reunified the estate except for the buildings, which were retained by the previous owners. The Baron's last descendent sold them to Henri Martin in 1981, who completed his purchase by buying the vineyard in 1982. Château Saint-Pierre, which had become a patchwork of vineyard plots over the centuries, was finally reunited.

Today, Françoise and Jean-Louis Triaud, assisted by their children, Vanessa and Jean, continue the family tradition with passion.

| | |
|---|---|
| Area under vine | 17 hectares |
| Production | 70,000 bottles |
| Soil | Gravel from the Günz period on a clay-sand subsoil |
| Grape varieties | 75% Cabernet Sauvignon, 15% Merlot, 10% Cabernet franc |
| Barrel ageing | 14-16 months - New barrels: 50% |

Co-Manager: Françoise Triaud - Co-Manager: Jean Triaud - Co-Manager: Vanessa Triaud

Château Saint-Pierre 33250 Saint-Julien-Beychevelle
GSP: Latitude: 45.1484749 - Longitude: -0.7474929999999631
Tel. +33 (0)5 56 59 08 18 - Fax +33 (0)5 56 59 16 18
contact@domaines-martin.com - **www.domaines-henri-martin.com**

# CHÂTEAU TALBOT
## GRAND CRU CLASSÉ EN 1855

**SAINT-JULIEN**  *Owners: Nancy Bignon-Cordier and her family*

This imposing estate owes its name to Connétable Talbot, the English general and governor of the province of Guyenne who was defeated at the famous Battle of Castillon in 1453. Talbot's vines grow in an ideal location bordering the estuary, on some of the region's most highly prized gravelly rises which alone produce great wines. Talbot is one of the oldest estates in the Médoc, and its reputation has been unfailingly fine through the years. That is because the château has been in the hands of experienced managers, and always shown itself to be worthy of its inclusion in the 1855 classification.

Owners of Talbot since the early 20th century, the Cordier family have perpetuated the commitment to quality of their predecessors. At Talbot, wine is very much past, present, and future. Therefore, tradition and technical innovations both count a great deal.

Thanks to an alliance between man and nature, and generations of experience, this outstanding terroir produces wines that may vary depending on the vintage, but is always well-balanced and complex. Five hectares are given over to the production of a dry white wine, Caillou Blanc, which is crisp and well-balanced. It likewise reflects its noble terroir.

| | |
|---|---|
| Area under vine | 104 hectares |
| Production | 325,000 bottles |
| Soil | Médoc gravel |
| Grape varieties | 68% Cabernet Sauvignon, 28% Merlot, 4% Petit Verdot |
| Barrel ageing | 14-16 months - New barrels: 50% |
| Second wine | Connétable Talbot |

Château Talbot 33250 Saint-Julien-Beychevelle
GPS: Latitude: 45.1576355 - Longitude: -0.75815714
Tel. +33 (0)5 56 73 21 50 - Fax. +33 (0)5 56 73 21 51
chateau-talbot@chateau-talbot.com - **www.chateau-talbot.com**

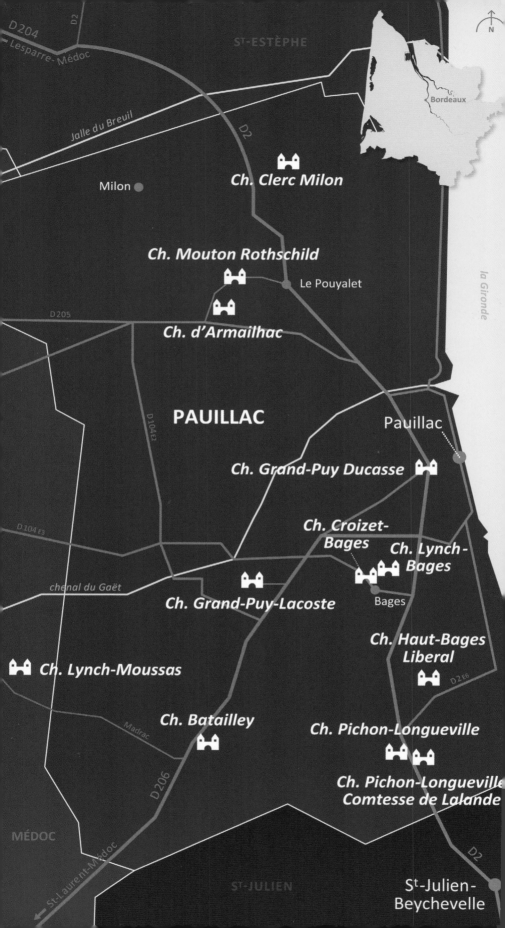

# CRUS DE PAUILLAC

Pauillac had a busy port from the dawn of history until the 21$^{st}$ century thanks to its privileged location halfway between the mouth of the Gironde estuary and the city of Bordeaux. Many ships stopped over before going upriver to Bordeaux or else out to sea.

Winegrowing in Pauillac dates back to the Late Middle Ages and developed significantly over the centuries. However, it was the creation of large estates from the early 17$^{th}$ century to the late 19$^{th}$ century that gave Pauillac the importance it has today. It is also the commune with the greatest number of first growths in the 1855 classification.

# CHÂTEAU D'ARMAILHAC
## GRAND CRU CLASSÉ EN 1855

Owner: Baronne Philippine de Rothschild G.F.A.

A *Grand Cru Classé* of the 1855 classification , Château d'Armailhac, a neighbour of Château Mouton Rothschild in Pauillac, has 70 hectares of vines planted with classic Bordeaux varieties: Cabernet Sauvignon, Merlot, Cabernet Franc and Petit Verdot.

Matured in oak barrels, the wine combines finesse and elegance with the power and tannins of Pauillac's great wines. Widely recognized for the quality of its wine, the estate has evolved over the years and incorporated numerous winemaking innovations.

Baron Philippe acquired Château d'Armailhac in 1933. Also well-known for its grounds, front courtyard and house, the château had belonged to the d'Armailhacq family since the 18th century. Known as Château Mouton d'Armailhacq between 1956 and 1989, it was then successively named Château Mouton Baron Philippe and Château Mouton Baronne Philippe.

In 1989, Baroness Philippine de Rothschild revived the historic link with the original owner by renaming the estate Château d'Armailhac. Continuity is ensured today by Baroness Philippine's children, Camille Sereys de Rothschild, Philippe Sereys de Rothschild and Julien de Beaumarchais de Rothschild.

146

| | |
|---|---|
| Area under vine | 70 hectares |
| Soil | Gravel and clay-limestone |
| Grape varieties | 52% Cabernet Sauvignon, 36% Merlot, 10% Cabernet franc, 2% Petit Verdot |
| Barrel ageing | 12 months - New barrels: 33% |

Managing Director: Philippe Dhalluin – Technical Director: Jean-Paul Polaert - Commercial Director: Hervé Gouin

Château d'Armailhac 33250 Pauillac
GPS: Latitude: 45.1992039 - Longitude: -0.7488862
Tel. +33 (0)5 56 73 20 20 – Fax +33 (0)5 56 59 16 32
webmaster@bphr.com - **www.chateau-darmailhac.com**

# CHÂTEAU BATAILLEY
## GRAND CRU CLASSÉ EN 1855

Château Batailley, a fifth growth in the 1855 classification, is one of the jewels of the Castéja family and the firm of Borie-Manoux.

The name of this estate comes from the word "bataille", meaning battle, in memory of a skirmish that took place in the vines in 1453 during the Hundred Years' War. During this battle, the French troops retook possession of Château Latour which was occupied by the English, and this marked the end of English rule over the Medoc region.

The estate as we know it today was created from the 16th to the 18th centuries on this land full of history. The château grounds were designed in the 19th century by Barillet-Deschamps, a famous landscape artist during the reign of Napoléon III.

Batailley is a classic Pauillac, with a deep ruby-red colour, excellent structure and pronounced blackcurrant overtones.

| | |
|---|---|
| Area under vine | 55 hectares |
| Soil | Pure gravel |
| Grape varieties | 70% Cabernet Sauvignon, 25% Merlot, 3% Cabernet franc, 2% Petit Verdot |
| Barrel ageing | 16-18 months - New barrels: 50-60% |

Managing Director: Philippe Castéja

Château Batailley 33250 Pauillac
GPS: Latitude: 45.1767988 - Longitude: -0.7732238
Tel. +33 (0)5 56 00 00 70 - Fax +33 (0)5 57 87 48 61
domaines@borie-manoux.fr - www.batailley.com

# CHÂTEAU CLERC MILON
## GRAND CRU CLASSÉ EN 1855

| PAUILLAC | Owner: Baronne Philippine de Rothschild G.F.A. |
|---|---|

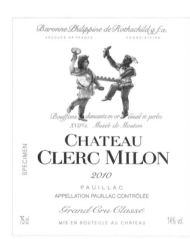

A *Grand Cru Classé* of the 1855 classification, Château Clerc Milon has 41 hectares of vines overlooking the Gironde estuary in the commune of Pauillac. With a superb terroir, thanks to the composition of the soil and exposure to sunlight, the vineyard is a close neighbour of two First Growths. Most of the vines are over 50 years old and represent a genetic treasure-house, including plantings of the historic but rare Carmenère grape.

Baron Philippe de Rothschild purchased Château Clerc Milon in 1970. Thanks to the energy of his daughter, Baroness Philippine de Rothschild, and a devoted winemaking team, the estate gradually experienced a renaissance. The vineyard was entirely restructured and many technical improvements were introduced, culminating in the construction in 2007 of a new vat room and cutting-edge winemaking facilities. The various changes have borne fruit, and Château Clerc Milon has become a new benchmark for the Médoc.

Today, Camille Sereys de Rothschild, Philippe Sereys de Rothschild and Julien de Beaumarchais de Rothschild are continuing the work of their mother, Baroness Philippine.

148

| Area under vine | 41 hectares |
|---|---|
| Soil | Gravel and clay-limestone |
| Grape varieties | 50% Cabernet Sauvignon, 37% Merlot, 10% Cabernet franc, 2% Petit Verdot, 1% Carmenère |
| Barrel ageing | 16-18 months - New barrels: 50% |

Managing Director: Philippe Dhalluin – Director: Jean-Emmanuel Danjoy - Commercial Director: Hervé Gouin

Château Clerc Milon 33250 Pauillac
GPS: Latitude: 45.2214335 - Longitude: -0.7646710
Tel. +33 (0)5 56 73 20 20
visites@bphr.com - www.chateau-clerc-milon.com

# CHÂTEAU CROIZET-BAGES

## GRAND CRU CLASSÉ EN 1855

| PAUILLAC | Owners: the Quié family |
|----------|------------------------:|

In the early 18th century, the Croizet brothers, both members of the Bordeaux parliament, consolidated a number of small vineyard plots in order to form a wine estate in the famous hamlet of Bages, in Pauillac. This estate was included among the fifth growths in the famous 1855 classification under the name of Château Croizet-Bages.

Jean-Baptiste Monnot, an American citizen and owner of the famous Klaxon brand, acquired Croizet Bages soon after the First World War. He in turn sold it to Paul Quié, owner of châteaux Rauzan-Gassies (a great growth of Margaux) and Bel Orme Tronquoy de Lalande, in 1942. Monsieur Quié undertook a renovation of the vineyard during the postwar period. This was completed by his son, Jean-Michel, who took over management in 1968.

Jean-Michel Quié is now assisted by his children, Anne-Françoise and Jean-Philippe, in overseeing the three family châteaux. Their passion for fine wine is very much in the tradition of the great growths of Bordeaux, and one of Jean-Michel Quié's greatest pleasures is to share his wine with people who are dear to him.

| | |
|---|---|
| Area under vine | 28.5 hectares |
| Production | 80,000 bottles |
| Soil | Deep gravel, gravel and sand |
| Grape varieties | 62% Cabernet Sauvignon, 28% Merlot, 6% Petit Verdot, 4% Cabernet franc |
| Barrel ageing | 12 months - New barrels: 50-55% |
| Second wine | Alias Croizet-Bages |

**Château Croizet-Bages** 9 rue du Port de la Verrerie - 33250 Pauillac
GPS: Latitude: 45.191553 - Longitude: -0.7587
Tel. +33 (0)5 56 59 01 62 - Fax +33 (0)5 56 59 23 39
croizetbages@domaines-quie.com - **www.croizetbages.fr**

# CHÂTEAU GRAND-PUY DUCASSE

## GRAND CRU CLASSÉ EN 1855

**PAUILLAC**

*Owner: CA Grands Crus*

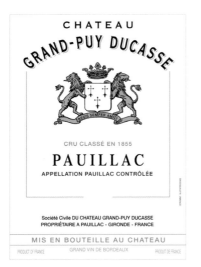

This classified growth consists of three large plots with some of the finest terroir in Pauillac: the northern plot is a neighbour of Mouton and Lafite, the central plot is located in a part of the commune called Grand-Puy, and the southern plot is on the Saint-Lambert plateau. This unusual configuration was due to the estate's founder, Pierre Ducasse, an eminent lawyer who pieced together this splendid vineyard with land he inherited or purchased in the 18th century.

Grand-Puy Ducasse has recently entered a new phase of its history with a decided upswing in quality. This is largely thanks to a study of the potential of each vineyard plot and a change in vineyard management. The vines are now trained higher and each different grape variety has been perfectly matched to the most suitable terroir.

Ripe, healthy Cabernet Sauvignon and Merlot grapes, coupled with rigorous production methods, account for Grand Puy Ducasse's reputation for aromatic complexity, beautiful structure, and excellent ageing potential. It is the epitome of a fine Pauillac.

150

| | |
|---|---|
| Area under vine | 40 hectares |
| Production | 120,000 bottles |
| Soil | Garonne gravel and a mixture of silica and gravel |
| Grape varieties | 60% Cabernet Sauvignon, 40% Merlot |
| Barrel ageing | 18 months - New barrels: 40% |
| Second wine | Prélude à Grand-Puy Ducasse |

Managing Director: Thierry Budin

Château Grand-Puy Ducasse 4 quai Antoine Ferchaud - 33250 Pauillac
GPS: Latitude: 45.1997883 - Longitude: -0.7461077
Tel. +33 (0)5 56 59 00 40 - Fax +33 (0)5 56 59 36 47
contact@cagrandscrus.com - **www.cagrandscrus.com**

# CHÂTEAU GRAND-PUY-LACOSTE

## GRAND CRU CLASSÉ EN 1855

**PAUILLAC**                                        *Owner: François-Xavier Borie*

The name Grand-Puy ("puy" comes from the Latin word *podium*, meaning hill) describes this vineyard's privileged location overlooking Pauillac, where the château reigns over a sea of vines. Included in the famous 1855 classification, Grand-Puy-Lacoste has had an important role to play in the history of Bordeaux wine since the early 16th century. It previously belonged to a family who contributed several members to the Bordeaux parliament. They fell in love with the magnificent gravel terroir and were responsible for establishing the wine's fine reputation. They were followed by several other families: the Lacostes (who gave the estate its definitive name), the Saint-Guirons, and the Saint-Legiers.

In 1930, the château's history was marked by the arrival of Raymond Dupin, an unusual character and bon vivant who remained the owner until 1978. Shortly before his death, he sold Grand-Puy-Lacoste to the Borie family because he appreciated their rigour and devotion to producing fine great growth wine in the Médoc.
François-Xavier Borie, the present owner, is behind this superb estate's renaissance. He has made major investments and constantly improved the quality of Grand-Puy-Lacoste in order to reflect all the finesse of its great Pauillac terroir.

| | |
|---|---|
| Area under vine | 55 hectares |
| Production | 180,000 bottles |
| Soil | Very deep coarse gravel |
| Grape varieties | 75 % Cabernet Sauvignon, 20 % Merlot, 5 % Cabernet franc |
| Barrel ageing | 16-18 months - New Barrels: 75% |
| Second wine | Lacoste-Borie |

Château Grand-Puy-Lacoste Domaines François-Xavier Borie - BP 82 - 33250 Pauillac - France
GPS: Latitude: 45.189545 - Longitude: -0.766758
Tel. +33 (0)5 56 59 06 66 - Fax +33 (0)5 56 59 22 27
dfxb@domainesfxborie.com - **www.grand-puy-lacoste.com**

# CHÂTEAU HAUT-BAGES LIBÉRAL
## GRAND CRU CLASSÉ EN 1855

**PAUILLAC**

*Owner: Claire Villars Lurton*

The Libéral family founded the estate in the 18th century. Generation after generation, they succeeded in forming a vineyard with the best soils of Pauillac. Château Haut-Bages Libéral was included among the fifth growths in 1855. This superb estate was renovated in 1960 when the Cruse family, who also owned Château Ponet-Canet at the time, undertook far-reaching replanting. Since the arrival of the Villars-Merlaut family in 1983, Haut-Bages Libéral has gradually recovered its formal glory.

Château Haut-Bages Libéral has 30 hectares of vines overlooking the Gironde River. Half of this area, located right next to Château Latour, features gravel on limestone and clay, and the other part, on the plateau of Bages, has deep gravels soil.

Today, Claire Villars Lurton is the owner of Château Haut-Bages Libéral. She modernised the winemaking facilities and introduced biodynamic and environmentally-friendly methods. She is committed to making the most of the terroir thanks to a very quality-oriented approach devoted to restoring the estate's prestige.

152

| | |
|---|---|
| Area under vine | 30 hectares |
| Production | 120,000 bottles |
| Soil | Garonne gravel on clay-limestone |
| Grape varieties | 70% Cabernet Sauvignon, 30% Merlot |
| Barrel ageing | 16 months - New barrels: 40% |
| Seconds vins | La Fleur de Haut-Bages Libéral - Le Pauillac de Haut-Bages Libéral - La Chapelle de Bages |

Château Haut-Bages Libéral 33250 Pauillac
GPS: Latitude: 45.182445 - Longitude: -0.746995
Tel. +33 (0)5 57 88 76 65 - Fax +33 (0)5 57 88 98 33
infos@hautbagesliberal.com - **www.hautbagesliberal.com**

# CHÂTEAU LYNCH-BAGES
## GRAND CRU CLASSÉ EN 1855

A stone's throw from Pauillac and overlooking the Gironde estuary, the Lynch-Bages winery (1855 Grand Cru Classé) lies on the Bages plateau – one of the commune's finest gravel croupes. Formerly the property of the illustrious Lynch family from Ireland, the estate was repurchased in 1934 by Jean-Charles Cazes. Housed in a building that dates back to the late 16th century, the old Lynch-Bages vatting room that was installed in the 1850s is one of the few old wine-making facilities that has remained intact. A visit here is a veritable voyage in time.

A lover of both history and the art of living, Jean-Michel Cazes has created numerous activities combining wine and the world of culture and brought them together under the Lynch-Bages & Cie label. These include, for example, the Relais & Châteaux Cordeillan-Bages (Michelin® 2-star restaurant, 2015) and its cookery school, the VINIV cellar for personal wine-making, the Cercle Lynch-Bages wine-tasting school, and the businesses and various public spaces that are now the hub of the village of Bages. Jean-Michel Cazes handed over to his son Jean-Charles back in 2006, and the Lynch-Bages wines continue to bear witness to the same generosity and excellence, benefitting as they do from the same high standards.

| | |
|---|---|
| Area under vine | 100 hectares |
| Production | 350,000 bottles |
| Soil | Garonne gravel |
| Grape varieties | 72% Cabernet Sauvignon, 20% Merlot, 5% Cabernet franc, 3% Petit Verdot |
| Barrel ageing | 12-18 months - New barrels: 70% |
| Second wine | Echo de Lynch-Bages |

Managing Director: Jean-Charles Cazes

Château Lynch-Bages 33250 Pauillac
GPS: Latitude: 45.191822 - Longitude: -0.754296
Tel. +33 (0)5 56 73 24 00 - Fax +33 (0)5 56 59 26 42
contact@lynchbages.com - **www.lynchbages.com**

# Château Lynch-Moussas

## Grand Cru Classé en 1855

Owners: the Castéja heirs

GRAND CRU CLASSÉ EN 1855

CHATEAU
**LYNCH-MOUSSAS**

PAUILLAC
2009

The name Lynch-Moussas goes back to the 19th century, when Count Lynch's estate was divided in two: Lynch-Bages and Lynch-Moussas (Moussas is the place name where many of the vines are located).

The Castéja family, Pauillac land owners since the 17th century, acquired this château in the early 20th century. Émile Castéja inherited the estate, as well as management, in 1970. He immediately set about enhancing its development. His son, Philippe Castéja, has managed this and all the family's Left Bank estates estate since 2001.

This date coincides with the creation of a second wine, Les Hauts de Lynch-Moussas. Château Lynch-Moussas is one of the only family-owned estaets to be sold on the Bordeaux market.

| Area under vine | 55 hectares |
|---|---|
| Soil | Pure gravel |
| Grape varieties | 70% Cabernet Sauvignon, 30% Merlot |
| Barrel ageing | 14-18 months - New barrels: 55% |
| Second wine | Les Hauts de Lynch-Moussas |

Managing Director: Philippe Castéja

Château Lynch-Moussas 33250 Pauillac
GPS: Latitude: 45.2022481 - Longitude: -0.8349154
Tel. +33 (0)5 56 00 00 70 - Fax +33 (0)5 57 87 48 61
domaines@borie-manoux.fr - **www.lynch-moussas.com**

# CHÂTEAU PICHON BARON
## GRAND CRU CLASSÉ EN 1855

| PAUILLAC | Owner: AXA Millésimes |
|---|---|

Château Pichon Baron, Second Cru Classé in 1855, is one of the great historic vineyards of Bordeaux.

The great terroir comprising the 30-hectare plateau of Pichon Baron (one of the estate's historic plots which was already in use when the wine was first produced in 1694) is devoted entirely to production of the Grand Vin and now represents the major part of the blend.

A rigorous selection policy in the vineyard and in the cellars ensures the production of Château Pichon Baron which is the pure expression of our unique terroir. This wine with an exceptionally long finish displays truly regal power and characteristically noble finesse and elegance.

The château was built in 1851. It boasts a superb view over the Gironde estuary and fairytale architecture with slender turrets and a reflecting water pond. Opening the château up to wine lovers from all four corners of the world is one of our priorities. The quality of our events organisation was rewarded by a Golden Trophy at the Best of Wine Tourism Awards 2011.

| | |
|---|---|
| Area under vine | 73 hectares |
| Production | 170,000 bottles |
| Soil | Garonne gravel |
| Grape varieties | 62% Cabernet Sauvignon, 33% Merlot, 3% Cabernet franc, 2% Petit Verdot |
| Barrel ageing | 20 months - New barrels: 80% |
| Second wine | Les Griffons de Pichon Baron - Les Tourelles de Longueville |

Managing Director: Christian Seely - Technical Director: Jean-René Matignon

Château Pichon Baron BP 112 - 33250 Pauillac
GPS: Latitude: 45.176667 - Longitude: -0.751111
Tel. +33 (0)5 56 73 17 17 - Fax +33 (0)5 56 59 64 62
contact@pichonbaron.com - **www.pichonbaron.com**

# CHÂTEAU PICHON LONGUEVILLE
## COMTESSE DE LALANDE

**GRAND CRU CLASSÉ EN 1855**

**PAUILLAC**                                    *Owner: Champagne Louis Roederer*

Château Pichon Longueville Comtesse de Lalande has 89 hectares of vines in Pauillac, in the heart of the Médoc, ideally situated along the Gironde Estuary.

In three centuries, only two families have contributed to the worldwide reputation of the château and its wines.

The third family, owners of Champagne Louis Roederer, acquired the estate in January 2007. They aim to perpetuate the excellent work done by their predecessors and to attain the ultimate in quality and prestige.

Relying on the best of traditional and modern methods, Château Pichon Longueville Comtesse de Lalande built new winemaking facilities in 2013.

The wines epitomise the remarkable balance of Pauillac, with a silky tannic structure along with an expressive and suave aromatic complexity.

156

| | |
|---|---|
| Area under vine | 89 hectares |
| Production | 170,000 bottles |
| Soil | Garonne gravel on clay with a layer of soil rich in iron oxide |
| Grape varieties | 60% Cabernet Sauvignon, 29% Merlot, 7% Cabernet franc, and 4% Petit Verdot |
| Barrel ageing | 18-22 months - New barrels: 50% |
| Second wine | Réserve de la Comtesse |

Managing Director: Nicolas Glumineau

Château Pichon Longueville Comtesse de Lalande 33250 Pauillac
GPS: Latitude: 45.176814 - Longitude: -0.750132
Tel. +33 (0)5 56 59 19 40 - Fax +33 (0)5 56 59 26 56
pichon@pichon-lalande.com - **www.pichon-lalande.com**

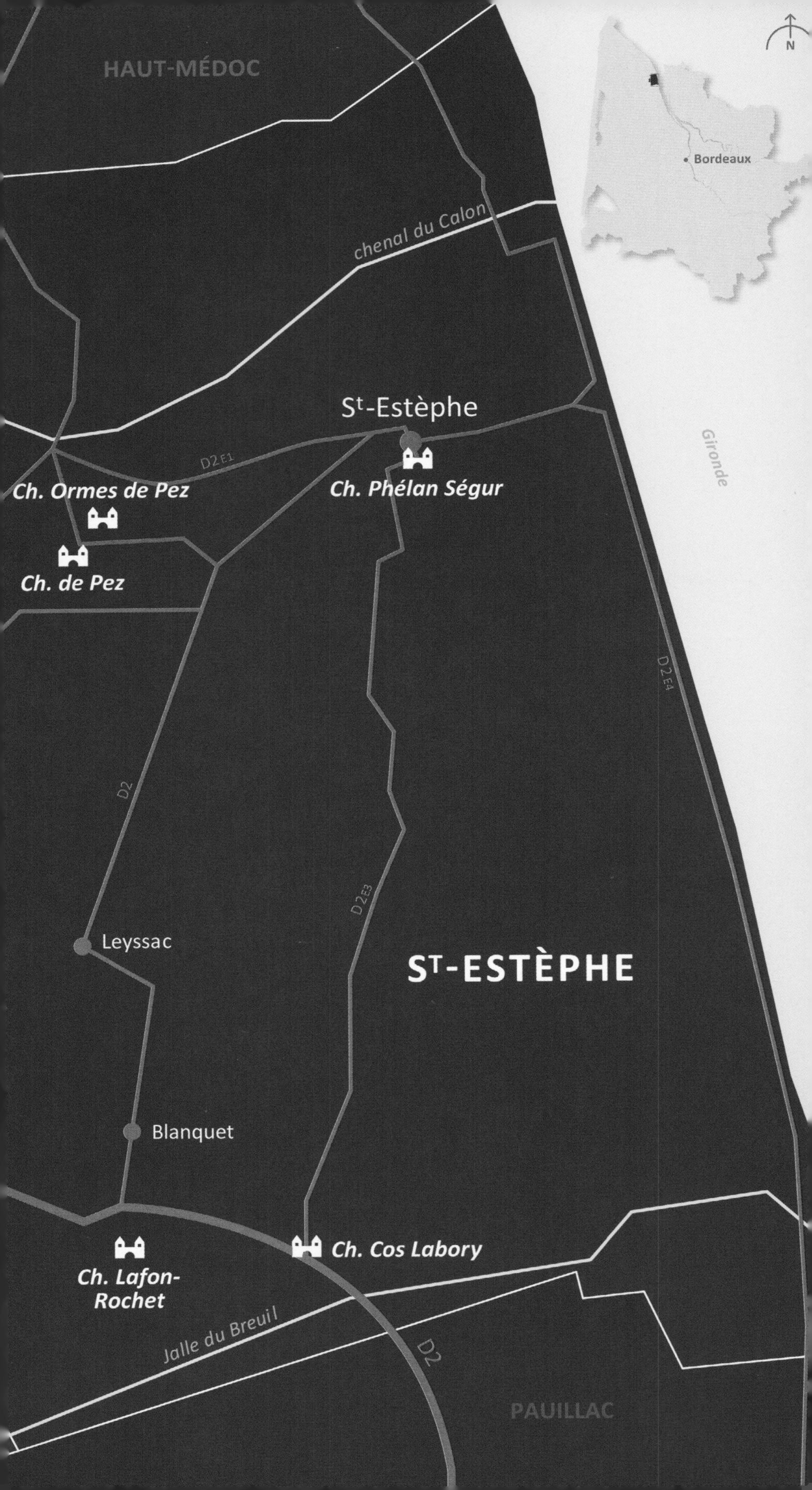

HAUT-MÉDOC

N

Bordeaux

chenal du Calon

St-Estèphe

D2E1

Ch. Ormes de Pez

Ch. Phélan Ségur

Ch. de Pez

Gironde

D2E4

D2

D2E3

St-ESTÈPHE

Leyssac

Blanquet

Ch. Cos Labory

Ch. Lafon-
Rochet

Jalle du Breuil

D2

PAUILLAC

# Crus de Saint-Estèphe

Saint-Estèphe is the northernmost appellation in the Haut-Médoc. It benefits from an outstanding location along the Gironde estuary, which can be seen from most of the commune's gravelly rises.

The first known inhabitants date back to the Bronze Age, and vines were planted here during the Roman occupation at the beginning of the Common Era.

The 17th, 18th and 19th centuries saw the development of grands crus which, as in the other famous communal appellations in the Médoc and helped by the Bordeaux négociants who aged and sold the wines, contributed greatly to the reputation of Saint-Estèphe around the world.

# CHÂTEAU COS LABORY

## GRAND CRU CLASSÉ EN 1855

| SAINT-ESTÈPHE | *Owner: the Audoy family* |
|---|---|

Château Cos Labory takes its name to the word "caux", meaning "stony hill," and to François Labory, who owned the estate from 1820 to 1840. Purchased in 1845 by Monsieur d'Estournel, Cos Labory was sold in 1852 to Charles Martyns, an English banker. Included in the famous 1855 classification, this great growth belongs to the Audoy family for over half a century.

Located on the famous gravelly rise of Cos, the eighteen-hectare vineyard benefits from remarkable sun exposure. It is planted with traditional grape varieties.

Major investments have been made over the past several years and Château Cos Labory now relies on the latest technology to produce their great wines.

Great attention is paid during fermentation and ageing, which are adapted to the character of each vintage. Cos Labory combines power, elegance, and the typical structure of a great Saint-Estèphe.

160

| | |
|---|---|
| Area under vine | 18 hectares |
| Production | 80,000 bottles |
| Soil | Günz gravel on a marl and limestone platform |
| Grape varieties | 60% Cabernet Sauvignon, 35% Merlot, 5% Cabernet franc |
| Barrel ageing | 18 months - New barrels: 50% |
| Second wine | Charme de Cos Labory |

Manager: Bernard Audoy

Château Cos Labory 33180 Saint-Estèphe
GPS: Latitude: 45.230717 - Longitude: -0.777014
Tel. +33 (0)5 56 59 30 22 - Fax +33 (0)5 56 59 73 52
contact@cos-labory.com - **www.cos-labory.com**

# CHÂTEAU LAFON-ROCHET
## GRAND CRU CLASSÉ EN 1855

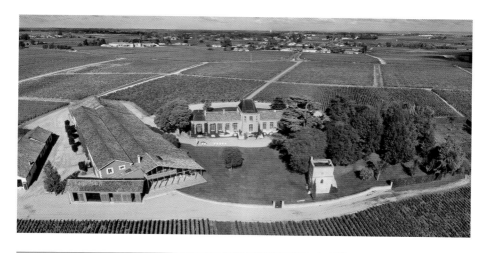

| | |
|---|---|
| SAINT-ESTÈPHE | *Owner: the Tesseron family* |

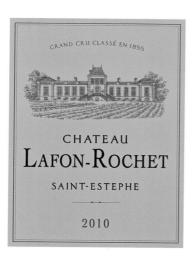

This estate can trace its history back to the latter 16th century. For over two hundred years, it belonged to the Lafon family, who managed to keep hold of it through the turmoil of the French Revolution. They also lived to see its ultimate recognition in the 1855 classification, when Lafon-Rochet was admitted to the very select club of great growths, one of only five in Saint-Estèphe. Ideally situated, between Cos d'Estournel and Lafite-Rothschild to the south, Lafon-Rochet features some of the finest vineyard land in the world. It is not hard to see why Guy Tesseron, well-known for the quality of his old Cognac, became interested in acquiring the estate over forty years ago.

He soon came to the conclusion that the existing buildings were not worthy of saving. He thus completely demolished them, going on to build a new cellar as well as a château based on the plans of a 17th century chartreuse, or manor house, that is unique in Bordeaux.

Thanks to unceasing care and attention, Lafon-Rochet is one of the finest wines in Saint-Estèphe, France, and the whole world.

| | |
|---|---|
| Area under vine | 40 hectares |
| Production | 100,000 bottles |
| Soil | Gravel from the Quaternary Period with a clay-limestone subsoil |
| Grape varieties | 55% Cabernet Sauvignon, 40% Merlot, 3% Cabernet franc, 2% Petit Verdot |
| Barrel ageing | 15 months - New barrels: 50% |
| Second wine | Les Pèlerins de Lafon Rochet |

Director: Basile Tesseron - Manager: Michel Tesseron - Manager: Caroline Poniatowski

Château Lafon-Rochet Blanquet ouest - 33180 Saint-Estèphe
GPS: Latitude: 45,2292655 - Longitude: -0,7833726
Tel. +33 (0)5 56 59 32 06 - Fax +33 (0)5 56 59 72 43
lafon@lafon-rochet.com - **www. lafon-rochet.com**

# CHÂTEAU ORMES DE PEZ

     *Owner: the Cazes family*

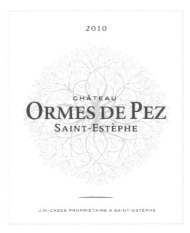

2010

CHÂTEAU
ORMES DE PEZ
SAINT-ESTÈPHE

J.M. CAZES PROPRIÉTAIRE À SAINT-ESTÈPHE

Dating back to the mid-18th century, Ormes de Pez was named after the tall, century-old elms growing there. Acquired by Jean-Charles Cazes in 1940, this was his second property, after Lynch-Bages in 1939.

Located on the outskirts of the hamlet of Pez, to the west of the commune of Saint-Estèphe, the estate is split into two quite distinct terroirs: plots of gravelly rises on quartz and river stones, which are perfect for the Cabernets, and cooler plots consisting of sand and clay, suitable for Merlot. The same high standards are applied here as at Château Lynch-Bages: from vineyard management to fermentation and ageing.

True expressions of their terroir, Les Ormes de Pez has a spicy, voluptuous character with great tannic structure.

The 18th century manor house and its adjoining outbuildings, cellars, and low stone walls blend in beautifully with the estate's 40 hectares of vines. In addition, the château's five guest rooms provide a calm and relaxing atmosphere in lovely setting.

This is the perfect place for creating a great wine as well as enjoying a delightful stay at the heart of the wine country.

162

| | |
|---|---|
| Area under vine | 40 hectares |
| Production | 240,000 bottles |
| Soil | Garonne gravel |
| Grape varieties | 50% Cabernet Sauvignon, 41% Merlot, 7% Cabernet franc, 2% Petit Verdot |
| Barrel ageing | 14-16 months - New barrels: 45% |

Managing Director: Jean-Charles Cazes

Château Ormes de Pez 33180 Saint-Estèphe
GPS: Latitude: 45.260593 - Longitude: -0.78975
Tel. +33 (0)5 56 73 24 00 - Fax +33 (0)5 56 59 26 42
contact@ormesdepez.com - **www.ormesdepez.com**

# Château de Pez

*Owner: Champagne Louis Roederer*

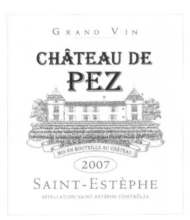

The Champagne house of Louis Roederer bought this beautiful, historic estate in June 1995.

Château de Pez is one of the oldest winegrowing properties in Saint-Estèphe. Created in the 15th century, it achieved fame in the 16th century when it was acquired by the Pontac family, who also founded Haut Brion. Initially a hunting lodge, the property was enlarged and transformed exclusively into a wine producing estate over time. Its architecture was also significantly modified in the 18th century. Two wings and two towers were added to the main building, which definitely took on the appearance of a château as a result. It was entirely renovated in 2000, as were the outbuildings and winemaking facilities.

Located west, on the heights of Saint-Estèphe, the vineyard consists of 38 hectares of gravelly soil on clay-limestone bedrock. The wines of château de Pez have wonderful tannic structure, power, a long aftertaste, a great deal of finesse, and excellent ageing potential.

| | |
|---|---|
| Area under vine | 38 hectares |
| Production | 160,000 bottles |
| Soil | Limestone gravel and clay |
| Grape varieties | 47% Cabernet Sauvignon, 44% Merlot, 6% Cabernet franc, 3% Petit Verdot |
| Barrel ageing | 12-18 months - New barrels: 40% |

Managing Director: Nicolas Glumineau

Château de Pez Lieu-dit Pez - 33180 Saint-Estèphe
GPS: Latitude: 45.2602074 - Longitude: -0.7898998
Tel. +33 (0)5 56 59 30 26 - Fax +33 (0)5 56 59 39 25
pmoureau@chateaudepez.com - **www.chateaudepez.com**

163

# Château Phélan Ségur

*Owners: Gardinier & Sons*

Located in the village of Saint-Estèphe, Château Phélan Ségur has proudly overlooked the Gironde estuary since the early 19th century. Its history is intimately linked with that of the Médoc. Founded by Irishman Bernard Phelan when he united Clos de Garramey and Domaine Ségur de Cabanac, the estate was developed by his son, Frank, and renamed Phélan Ségur in the early 20th century.

Consisting of seventy hectares of vines divided into four distinct parts, the great diversity of the terroir accounts for Phélan Ségur's complexity. The cellar and vat room are integrated into the château in a highly unusual architectural ensemble. The wines are aged with the greatest of care and Phélan Ségur is famous for its elegance, finesse, and balance.

Belonging to the family-owned Gardinier group specialised in prestigious hotels and restaurants, Château Phélan Ségur has raised the art of hospitality to new heights.

| | |
|---|---|
| Area under vine | 70 hectares |
| Production | 200,000 bottles |
| Soil | Gravel and clay |
| Grape varieties | 55% Cabernet Sauvignon, 43% Merlot, and 1% Cabernet Franc |
| Barrel ageing | 18 months - New barrels: 50% |
| Second wine | Frank Phélan |

President: Thiery Gardinier - Managing Director: Véronique Dausse

Château Phélan Ségur 33180 Saint-Estèphe
GPS: Latitude : 45.2617 - Longitude : -0.7696
Tel. +33 (0)5 56 59 74 00 - Fax +33 (0)5 56 59 74 10
phelan@phelansegur.com - **www.phelansegur.com**

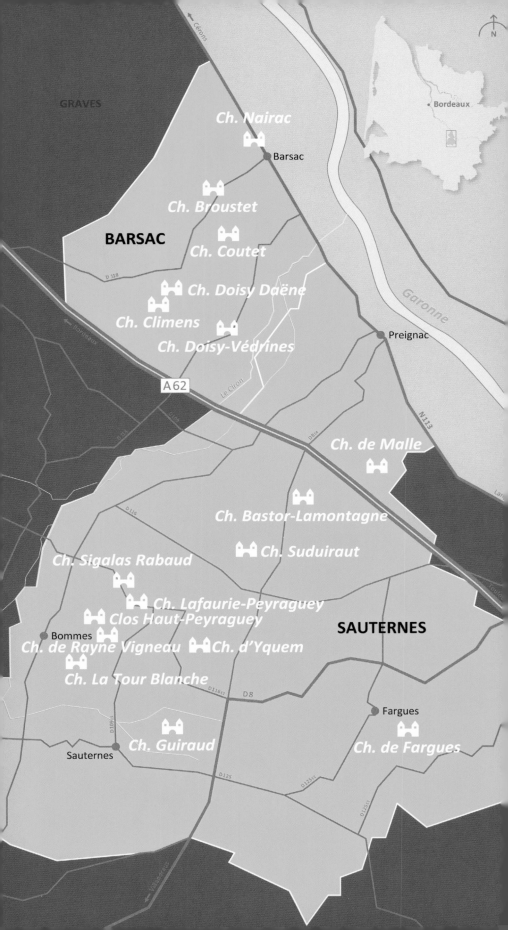

# CRUS DE SAUTERNES ET DE BARSAC

The Sauternes appellation consists of five communes: Sauternes, Fargues, Bommes, Preignac, and Barsac. Barsac has its own separate appellation as well.

Sauternes produces precious nectar that is known all over the world and considered the finest white wine in the world by many connoisseurs. Furthermore, the jewel of Sauternes, Château d'Yquem, was the only estate in either the Médoc or Sauternes to be classified a "Premier Cru Supérieur" in 1855.

The appellation is separated from the Graves on its western side by the Ciron valley. The river Ciron is responsible for the microclimate particularly conducive to *Botrytis cinerea*, a fungus that concentrates the grapes and produces outstanding wines.

# CHÂTEAU BASTOR-LAMONTAGNE

*Owner: Motier Domaines*

Located in Preignac, one of the five communes in the Sauternes appellation, Château Bastor-Lamontagne has 52 hectares of vineyards in a single block on siliceous-gravel soil that produces rich, vigorous wines. The estate takes its name from Chevalier de la Montaigne, a councillor of the Bordeaux Parliament who became the owner in 1711. It was named "Bastore" on Belleyme's famous late 18th century map, and was already quite large. The château took on greater importance in the 19th century thanks to Amédée Larrieu, who also owned Château Haut-Brion in Pessac.

Château Bastor-Lamontagne has always given priority to fruit expression and balance. Often considered a "modern Sauternes", it is elegant, harmonious, and enjoyable at any time of the day. Although it can age very well, Bastor-Lamontagne is also delicious young thanks to its vivaciousness and finesse.

A new chapter in the château's history was begun in 2014 when the property was acquired by the Moulin and Cathiard families, who have brought with them considerable enthusiasm and experience.

| | |
|---|---|
| Area under vine | 52 hectares |
| Production | 60-80,000 bottles |
| Soil | Siliceous-gravel and clay-gravel |
| Grape varieties | 80% Sémillon, 20% Sauvignon blanc |
| Barrel ageing | 16 months - New barrels: 30% |
| Second wine | Les Remparts de Bastor-Lamontagne |

Joint managers: Augustin Belloy - Daniel Cathiard - Managing Director: Michel Garat

Château Bastor-Lamontagne 33210 Preignac
GPS: Latitude: 44.584982 - Longitude: -0.2954852
Tel. +33 (0)5 56 63 27 66 - Fax +33 (0)5 56 76 87 03
bastor@bastor-lamontagne.com - **www.bastor-lamontagne.com**

# CHÂTEAU BROUSTET
## GRAND CRU CLASSÉ EN 1855

## SAUTERNES
*Owner: Vignobles de Terroirs*

In the early 19th century, Monsieur Capdeville, the owner of Château Broustet, acquired the neighbouring estate, Château Nairac. This is why it was referred to as "Broustet-Nairac" when it was ranked a second growth in the 1855 classification.

The Fournier family acquired Chateau Broustet in the late 19th century and set up a cooperage there. The model for the 225-litre barrique bordelaise, or Bordeaux barrel is said to have been created at Broustet, an explanation backed up by documents in the archives of the Bordeaux Chamber of Commerce.

Located in Barsac, this magnificent property has belonged to Vignobles de Terroirs since 2010. The vineyard has two types of soil: clay-limestone and gravel.

At the end of summer, morning mists warmed by the sun are conducive to the early and slow development of noble rot. The pebbles and topazes scattered around the vineyard store the sun's heat and release it at night, which is ideal for producing overripe grapes. Once botrytised, these are picked by hand in several waves. This results in an outstanding wine.

| | |
|---|---|
| Area under vine | 18 hectares |
| Production | 27,000 bottles |
| Soil | Clay-limestone, alluvial gravel |
| Grape varieties | 70% Sémillon, 20% Sauvignon, 10% Muscadelle |
| Barrel ageing | 22 months - New barrels: 40% |
| Second wine | Les Charmes de Château Broustet |

Manager: Pierre Mauget - Technical Manager: Jérémie Gravier

Château Broustet 33720 Barsac
GPS: Latitude: 44.603791 - Longitude: -0.325685
Tel. +33 (0)5 47 74 78 00 - Fax +33 (0)5 56 32 85 83
broustet@vignoblesdeterroirs.com - **www.vignoblesdeterroirs.com**

# CHÂTEAU CLIMENS
## PREMIER GRAND CRU CLASSÉ EN 1855

**BARSAC**                                              *Owner: Bérénice Lurton*

2009

*Château Climens*

1ᴱᴿ CRU · BARSAC
GRAND VIN DE SAUTERNES

BÉRÉNICE LURTON

A first growth Sauternes since 1855, Château Climens has long been called the "Lord of Barsac" due to the incomparable elegance and freshness of its wines.

Climens' strong personality is derived above all from its unique limestone terroir and the unfailing professionalism of successive winemaking teams. Lucien Lurton, an emblematic winegrowing figure, purchased Chateau Climens in 1971. The estate was taken over by his youngest daughter in 1992.

Assisted by her team, Bérénice Lurton manages Climens with the respect and tenacity it takes to make the most of this unique terroir. It is in this spirit that the estate has been entirely cultivated according to biodynamic principles since 2010.

| | |
|---|---|
| Area under vine | 30 hectares |
| Production | 30,000 bottles |
| Soil | Red ferruginous clay and sand on a fissured limestone shelf |
| Grape varieties | 100% Sémillon |
| Barrel ageing | 20-24 months - New barrels: 30% |
| Second wine | Cyprès de Climens |

Technical Director: Frédéric Nivelle - Commercial development and communication: Virginie Achou-Lepage

**Château Climens** 6 rue Plantey - 33720 Barsac
GPS: Latitude: 44.5896355 - Longitude: -0.3345215
Tel. +33 (0)5 56 27 15 33 - Fax +33 (0)5 56 27 21 04
contact@chateau-climens.fr - **www.chateau-climens.fr**

# CHÂTEAU COUTET
## PREMIER GRAND CRU CLASSÉ EN 1855

**BARSAC**  Owners: Philippe Baly - Dominique Baly

Recognised amongst the finest wines in its appellation, Château Coutet was classified a First Growth in 1855. One of the oldest estates in the Sauternes region, Coutet has an exceptional terroir and a rich architectural heritage. An English fortress in the 13th Century, this citadel with its square tower, a design typical of the era's military constructions, became a wine producing estate in 1643.

Château Coutet belonged to the de Lur Saluces family for over a century and currently is owned and managed by Philippe and Dominique Baly, with the technical and commercial collaboration of the Baron Philippe de Rothschild S.A., the vineyard's exclusive distributor.

The name Coutet comes from the Gascon word for knife ("couteau"), in reference to the wine's fresh, lively acidity and unique vivacity. In its youth, Château Coutet displays aromas of white flowers, citrus, honey, and vanilla. Age enhances the botrytis character to give the wines a deep, delicate bouquet with hints of spice and candied fruit.

| | |
|---|---|
| Area under vine | 38.5 hectares |
| Production | 42,000 bottles |
| Soil | Clay on a limestone subsoil |
| Grape varieties | 75% Sémillon, 23% Sauvignon Blanc, 2% Muscadelle |
| Barrel ageing | 18 months - New barrels: 100% |
| Second wine | La Chartreuse de Coutet |

Marketing and Communication: Aline Baly

Château Coutet 33720 Barsac
GPS: Latitude: 44.5945998 - Longitude: -0.3251383
Tel. +33 (0)5 56 27 15 46 - Fax +33 (0)5 56 27 02 20
info@chateaucoutet.com - **www.chateaucoutet.com**

# CHÂTEAU DOISY DAËNE

### GRAND CRU CLASSÉ EN 1855

## BARSAC

*Owner: Denis Dubourdieu*

Château Doisy Daëne, included among the second growths in the 1855 classification, is located on the Barsac limestone plateau in the Sauternes appellation. It has belonged to the Dubourdieu family since 1924. Four generations have made fine white wine here from father to son: Georges (1924-1948), Pierre (1949-1999) and Denis Dubourdieu since the 2000 vintage – assisted by his sons, Fabrice and Jean-Jacques. The family is committed to defending and promoting Doisy Daëne's image around the world. Denis Dubourdieu is also a professor of oenology at Bordeaux University and an internationally renowned consultant.

Château Doisy Daëne's 17.2 hectares of vines (87% Sémillon and 13% Sauvignon Blanc) are over 40 years old.

The wines have their own special style, with bright fruit concentrated by "noble rot" as well as lively acidity, excellent balance, and delicate flavours. Doisy Daëne's much-appreciated personality reflects both its excellent limestone terroir and a long family tradition of quality.

172

| | |
|---|---|
| Area under vine | 17.2 hectares |
| Production | 40,000 bottles |
| Soil | Clay-limestone |
| Grape varieties | 87% Sémillon, 13% Sauvignon |
| Barrel ageing | 18 months - New barrels: 33% |

Château Doisy Daëne 10 Gravas - 33720 Barsac
GPS: Latitude: 44.6093681 - Longitude: -0.3139061
Tel. +33 (0)5 56 62 96 51 - Fax +33 (0)5 56 62 14 89
reynon@wanadoo.fr - **www.denisdubourdieu.com**

# CHÂTEAU DOISY-VÉDRINES

## GRAND CRU CLASSÉ EN 1855

## SAUTERNES

The Chevaliers de Védrines owned this estate for centuries and gave their name to it. Included in the 1855 classification, it was acquired by the family of the present owners in the mid-19th century.

Doisy-Védrines is located on the clay-limestone rise in Haut Barsac. The soil is ploughed the traditional way and the grapes are picked by hand in several waves (up to 6 or 8). Fermentation and ageing take place in barrels (exclusively French oak).

The combination of modern and traditional techniques gives Château Doisy-Védrines its trademark richness and finesse typical of the great growths of Sauternes. Annual production amounts to 40,000 bottles.

When young, the wine is well-balanced and very pleasant, especially as an aperitif. Older vintages are a delight at the end of a meal.

| | |
|---|---|
| Area under vine | 35 hectares |
| Production | 40,000 bottles |
| Soil | Clay-limestone |
| Grape varieties | 80% Sémillon, 15% Sauvignon, 5% Muscadelle |
| Barrel ageing | 18 months - New barrels: 40-60% |
| Second wine | Château Petit Védrines |

Manager: Olivier Castéja

Château Doisy-Védrines Barsac - 33720 Podensac
GPS: Latitude: 44.5657 - Longitude: 0.2956
Tel. +33 (0)5 56 27 15 13 - Fax +33 (0)5 56 27 26 76
doisy-vedrines@orange.fr

# Château de Fargues

*Owner: Alexandre de Lur Saluces*

Built in 1306 par by cardinal Raymond Guilhem de Fargues, Château de Fargues came into the de Lur family in 1472 via marriage, and has been owned by the de Lur Saluces family since 1586. Overseen by Alexandre de Lur Saluces, a vast renovation project is breathing new life into the ancient fortress-castle severely damaged by fire in 1687, as well as the chapel. Château de Fargues covers some 180 hectares, but only the magnificent clay-gravel rise near the old castle is planted with vines.

Owners for over five centuries, the Lur Saluces family have perfected winemaking in complete harmony with noble rot. Absolute perfection is sought at all cost in every vintage, and the wine is not estate-bottled or sold under the château name if quality is not up to scratch (for example, there were no 1972, 1974, 1992, 2012 vintages of Château de Fargue.).

The grapes are picked meticulously in several waves and the wine is aged in barrel for thirty months to produce a wine of rare complexity with remarkably long ageing potential, like the other great wines produced by the Lur Saluces.

| Area under vine | 17 hectares |
|---|---|
| Production | 18,000 bottles |
| Soil | Gravel and clay |
| Grape varieties | 80% Sémillon, 20% Sauvignon Blanc |
| Barrel ageing | 30 months - New barrels: 30% |

Managing Director: Eudes d'Orléans - Manager: François Amirault - Representative Asia/USA: Philippe de Lur Saluces

Château de Fargues 33210 Fargues de Langon
GPS: Latitude: 44.535843 - Longitude: -0.295317
Tel. +33 (0)5 57 98 04 20 - Fax +33 (0)5 57 98 04 21
fargues@chateau-de-fargues.com - **www.chateau-de-fargues.com**

# CHÂTEAU GUIRAUD

## PREMIER GRAND CRU CLASSÉ EN 1855

Château Guiraud takes its name from a Bordeaux négociant, Pierre Guiraud, who purchased the estate in 1766. Included among the 1st growths in the 1855 classification, Château Guiraud has more than a hundred hectares of vines.

This magnificent property is well-known for their natural approach to viticulture. This includes the construction of insect hotels, planting five kilometres of hedges, developing genetic diversity, studying and propagating vines in a conservatory, etc.

Château Guiraud was the first among the 1st growths in the 1855 classification to be officially certified for organic viticulture in 2011.

The estate's ecological orientation helps to produce great wines with a strong personality and tremendous finesse. Château Guiraud is profound and well-focused with fruity and mineral flavours of extreme freshness.

| | |
|---|---|
| Area under vine | 100 hectares |
| Production | 100,000 bottles |
| Soil | Gravel with sand and clay |
| Grape varieties | 65% Sémillon, 35% Sauvignon Blanc |
| Barrel ageing | 18-24 months - New barrels: 100% |
| Second wine | Petit Guiraud |

Owners: Financière Guiraud (Xavier Planty - Olivier Bernard - Stephan von Neipperg - Robert Peugeot representing FFP)

Château Guiraud 33210 Sauternes
GPS: Latitude: 44.5328926 - Longitude: -0.3322452
Tel. +33 (0)5 56 76 61 01 - Fax +33 (0)5 56 76 67 52
carolinedegremont@chateauguiraud.com - **www.chateauguiraud.com**

175

# CLOS HAUT-PEYRAGUEY
## PREMIER GRAND CRU CLASSÉ EN 1855

**SAUTERNES**　　　　　　　　　　　　　　　　　*Owner: Bernard Magrez*

The word Peyraguey, meaning "hill" or "promontory", is a former barony acquired in the 18th century by the president of the Bordeaux parliament who was guillotined during the French Revolution. Shortly thereafter, the estate was acquired by Monsieur Lafaurie, and then became known as Pichard-Lafaurie.

From 1864 to 1879, the estate passed from the hands of Monsieur Saint Rieul Dupouy to those of Count Duchatel. When the Count died, it was divided in two. This was the beginning of Clos Haut Peyraguey, the smallest of the Sauternes first growths. The vineyard is located on the highest part of the commune of Bommes, and has a tremendous terroir. The château was later acquired by Monsieur Grillon, a Parisian pharmacist.

In 1914, Eugène Garbay, the great-grandfather of Jacques Pauly (who already owned Château Haut-Bommes) bought Clos Haut Peyraguey with Fernand Ginestet. In late 2012, this Sauternes first growth was acquired by Bernard Magrez. In doing so, he became the only person to own four classified growths in Bordeaux's four most prestigious appellations. The wines presently produced in Sauternes are Clos Haut Peyraguey, a first growth in the 1855 classification, and a second wine, Symphonie de Haut Peyraguey.

176

| | |
|---|---|
| Area under vine | 16.5 hectares |
| Production | 20,000 bottles |
| Soil | Sand and gravel with a clay subsoil |
| Grape varieties | 95% Sémillon, 5% Sauvignon Blanc |
| Barrel ageing | 20 months - New barrels: 30% |
| Second wine | Symphonie de Haut Peyraguey |

Estate Manager: Anthony Defives

Clos Haut-Peyraguey 1 Haut Peyraguey - 33210 Bommes
GPS : Latitude : 44.545806 - Longitude : -0.339208
Tél. +33 (0)5 56 76 61 53 - Fax +33 (0)5 56 76 69 65
closhautpeyraguey@pape-clement.com - **www.bernard-magrez.com**

# CHÂTEAU LAFAURIE-PEYRAGUEY

### PREMIER GRAND CRU CLASSÉ EN 1855

CHÂTEAU
**LAFAURIE-PEYRAGUEY**

2014

1ᵉʳ GRAND CRU CLASSÉ
SAUTERNES

Located in the middle of the finest terroir in the Sauternes appellation, Château Lafaurie-Peyraguey's vines grow on a gravel terrace 70 metres above sea level. The L'Enclos and Maisons Rouges plots represent the historic heart of the estate, with gravel soil from the Quaternary Period deposited over 600,000 years ago, as well as a substratum of Aquitaine limestone.

The winemaking facilities feature modern equipment to meet all legal and environmental standards, as well as air-conditioned ageing cellars with controlled humidity.

Owner Silvio Denz combines his passion for both winemaking and luxury goods at Lafaurie-Peyraguey. In keeping with creations by René Lalique, he designed an outstanding bottle based on an engraving entitled "Woman and Grapes" (dating from 28 September 1928) made on the woodwork of sleeping cars on the Côte d'Azur Pullman Express, which first saw service in 1929.

This engraving is to be found on bottles Château Lafaurie-Peyraguey starting with the 2013 vintage.

| | |
|---|---|
| Area under vine | 36 hectares |
| Production | 40,000 bottles |
| Soil | Clay and gravel as well as clay and sand |
| Grape varieties | 93% Sémillon, 6% Sauvignon Blanc, and 1% Muscadelle |
| Barrel ageing | 18 months - New barrels: 40% |
| Second wine | La Chapelle de Lafaurie-Peyraguey |

Manager: Éric Larramona – Cellarmaster : Vincent Despujos

Château Lafaurie-Peyraguey 33210 Bommes
GPS: Latitude: 44.549167 - Longitude: -0.337222
Tel. +33 (0)5 56 76 60 54 - Fax +33 (0)5 56 76 61 89
info@chateau-lafaurie-peyraguey.com - **www.chateau-lafaurie-peyraguey.com**

# CHÂTEAU DE MALLE
## GRAND CRU CLASSÉ EN 1855

| SAUTERNES | Owner: Countess de Bournazel |
|---|---|

Château de Malle, which dates back to 1540, has always remained in the same family: five generations of de Malle, six of de Lur Saluces and three of de Bournazel. The château and its Italian gardens embody all that is noble about wine. A visit to this beautiful historic monument, like no other in Southwest France, is strongly recommended. Few other places evoke tradition, an enviable lifestyle, and refinement as perfectly as Château de Malle.

Comprising some two hundred hectares, the estate is unusual in that it straddles both the Sauternes and Graves (red and white) appellations.

Château de Malle was included in the 1855 classification. Its light sandy and gravelly soil produces wines of great fruitiness. Very aromatic when young, with hints of ripe apricot, lime blossom, and acacia honey, Château de Malle is rich, distinguished, and relatively light. It is very open for the first five or six years after the vintage before shutting down, at which point it generally takes ten more years to reach its peak.

| Area under vine | 25 hectares |
|---|---|
| Production | 40,000 bottles |
| Soil | Siliceous and clay-gravel |
| Grape varieties | 69% Sémillon, 28% Sauvignon, 3% Muscadelle |
| Barrel ageing | 18-24 months - New barrels: 30% |
| Seconds vins | Sainte-Hélène du Château de Malle |

Managing Director: Paul-Henry de Bournazel - Reception: Cathy Maurey

Château de Malle route du château de Malle - 33210 Preignac
GPS: Latitude: 44.5657 - Longitude: -0.2956
Tel. +33 (0)5 56 62 36 86 - Fax +33 (0)5 56 76 82 40
accueil@chateau-de-malle.com - **www.chateau-de-malle.fr**

# CHÂTEAU NAIRAC

## GRAND CRU CLASSÉ EN 1855

Built at the end of the Ancien Régime by Jean Mollié, a disciple of Victor Louis, Château Nairac is named after a family of Huguenot ship owners who bought the property in 1777. The courtyard is flanked by outbuildings and cellars dating from the 17th century. As for the vineyard, records mention vines having grown here going back to the 16th century...

Included among the second growths in the 1855 classification, Nairac was noted as one of the finest wines in the region in the second edition of Cocks & Féret ("Bordeaux and its Wines") in 1868. After a series of crises, the estate was considerably renovated and rejuvenated in the 1970s. Thanks to owner Nicole Tari-Heeter and her three children, Nairac has since regained its former glory. Her son, Nicolas, has managed the estate with rigour and passion since 1993. Nairac is one of the finest wines of Barsac. As rich as the best châteaux in Sauternes, it displays a subtle difference due to its minerality, unique flavour profile, and elegant mouth feel. Everything possible is done to retain vintage character, respect nature, and reflect the terroir. The entire crop has been known to be declassified in vintages when there was no "noble rot".

Very much aware of their role as stewards of this historic estate, each member of the family exemplifies, in their own way, Nairac's motto: Inséparable d'une culture ("exemplifying a certain culture").

| | |
|---|---|
| Area under vine | 17 hectares |
| Production | 0-15,000 bottles |
| Soil | Grave and sand as well as clay and sand on asteriated limestone bedrock |
| Grape varieties | 90% Sémillon, 6% Sauvignon, 4% Muscadelle |
| Barrel ageing | 18-36 months - New barrels: 10-100% |
| Second wine | Esquisse de Nairac |

Estate Manager: Nicolas Heeter-Tari - Contact: Nicolas Heeter-Tari

Château Nairac 81 avenue Aristide Briand - 33720 Barsac
GPS: Latitude: 44.6098571 - Longitude: -0.3144207
Tel. +33 (0)5 56 27 16 16 - Fax +33 (0)5 56 27 26 50
chateau.nairac@wanadoo.fr - **www.chateaunairac.com**

# CHÂTEAU DE RAYNE VIGNEAU

## PREMIER GRAND CRU CLASSÉ EN 1855

**SAUTERNES** — *Owner: Financière Trésor du Patrimoine*

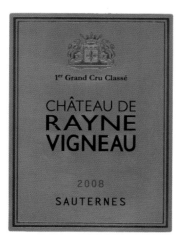

Located near the commune of Bommes, atop a magnificent gravelly rise overlooking the Sauternes region, Château Rayne Vigneau is the third highest point in the region, Yquem being the highest.

There have been generations of owners since this estate was founded in the early 17th century by Gabriel de Vigneau. The most famous was probably the Pontac family, whose name is inseparable from the creation of great Bordeaux wines. They acquired the property in 1834. Albert de Pontac, great-nephew of Madame de Rayne, née Catherine de Pontac, named the château Rayne Vigneau.

It was during his family's ownership that the estate was included among the first growths in the famous 1855 classification.

Château Rayne Vigneau is a unique and rare wine. According to legend, its soil contains gemstones that account for its incredible golden hue.

180

| | |
|---|---|
| Area under vine | 84 hectares |
| Production | 80,000 bottles |
| Soil | Clay gravel rises and a gravel plateau |
| Grape varieties | 80% Sémillon, 20% Sauvignon |
| Barrel ageing | 18 months - New barrels: 40-50% |
| Second wine | Madame de Rayne |

Administrator: Rémy Derek Smith

Château de Rayne Vigneau 33210 Bommes
GPS: Latitude: 44.5467126 - Longitude: -0.3570709
Tel. +33 (0)5 56 76 61 63 - Fax +33 (0)5 56 76 63 70
chateau@raynevigneau.fr - **www.raynevigneau.fr**

# CHÂTEAU SIGALAS RABAUD

## PREMIER GRAND CRU CLASSÉ EN 1855

| SAUTERNES | Owner: the Lambert des Granges family |
|---|---|

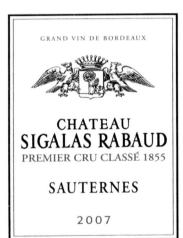

GRAND VIN DE BORDEAUX

## CHATEAU
## SIGALAS RABAUD
### PREMIER CRU CLASSÉ 1855

## SAUTERNES

### 2007

The configuration of Domaine de Rabaud, created in 1660, changed significantly in 1903 when Monsieur de Sigalas created a "jewel of a terroir" from clay-gravel plots in the southern part of the former Rabaud estate. These fourteen hectares formed a jewel of a vineyard, the smallest of the first growths in the 1855 classification.

Six generations later, the Marquis de Lambert des Granges and his daughter, Laure, now look after viticulture and winemaking with the same passion.

They produce a fine, fresh, elegant Sauternes whose structure is conferred by 85% Sémillon and charm by 15% Sauvignon Blanc. Sigalas-Rabaud is very refined – a true connoisseur's wine that is enjoyable when young thanks to a bouquet of lime blossom and white fruit, although it is frequently able to age for over a century. The second wine, Lieutenant de Sigalas, is the first growth's "little brother," made after a strict selection process. It combines the distinction of the *grand vin* with astonishing freshness.

This great terroir for white wines also produces two excellent dry white wines, Sémillante de Sigalas, made from old Sémillon vines, and Demoiselle de Sigalas, a blend of Sémillon and Sauvignon Blanc.

| | |
|---|---|
| Area under vine | 14 hectares |
| Production | 25,000 bottles |
| Soil | Gravel and clay |
| Grape varieties | 85% Sémillon, 15% Sauvignon |
| Barrel ageing | 20 months - New barrels: 33% |
| Second wine | Lieutenant de Sigalas |

Managing Director: Laure de Lambert Compeyrot – Oenologist for the *grand vin*: Éric Boissenot
Oenologist for the dry white wines: Jacques Lurton

Château Sigalas Rabaud 33210 Bommes
GPS: Latitude: 44.553808 - Longitude: -0.341295
Tel. +33 (0)5 56 21 31 43
contact@chateau-sigalas-rabaud.com - **www.chateau-sigalas-rabaud.fr**

# CHÂTEAU SUDUIRAUT

## PREMIER GRAND CRU CLASSÉ EN 1855

The team at the Suduiraut estate, passionate about their work are united in the pursuit of their goal: to extract from this great vineyard one of the world's finest wines.

Today, Château Suduiraut is acknowledged by all to be one of the finest Sauternes, thanks to a commitment to quality that is uncompromising in the extreme: strict choice of the plots of vines, meticulous harvesting methods, faultless control over fermentation in each individual barrel and a drastic selection process when the time comes to make the blend of the different wines.

Château Suduiraut is made from grapes selected from the finest terroirs of the property.

With an extensive life-span, it powerfully and harmoniously combines fruit and floral aromas with roasted and candied notes. Its superlative elegance comes from a match of total opposites: a voluptuous texture, mineral freshness and the heat of spices.

The château is a fine example of 17th-century architecture – distinguished, tasteful and luminous. It is surrounded by magnificent gardens designed by Le Nôtre, which add even more to the estate's charm.

182

| | |
|---|---|
| Area under vine | 92 hectares |
| Production | Varies from vintage to vintage |
| Soil | Sand and gravel |
| Grape varieties | 90% Sémillon, 10% Sauvignon Blanc |
| Barrel ageing | 18-24 months - New barrels: 50% |
| Second wine | Castelnau de Suduiraut - Les Lions de Suduiraut |

Managing Director: Christian Seely - Technical Director: Pierre Montégut

Château Suduiraut 33210 Preignac
GPS: Latitude: 44.557084 - Longitude: -0.318689
Tel. +33 (0)5 56 63 61 90 - Fax +33 (0)5 56 63 61 93
contact@suduiraut.com - www.suduiraut.com

# CHÂTEAU LA TOUR BLANCHE
## PREMIER GRAND CRU CLASSÉ EN 1855

**SAUTERNES**

*Owner: Conseil régional d'Aquitaine*

Founded in the 18th century, Château La Tour Blanche is located in the commune of Bommes, in the heart of the prestigious Sauternes appellation. A previous owner, Daniel "Osiris" Iffla, left the estate to the French government in 1907, on the condition that a tuition-free School of Viticulture and Oenology be created there.

The estate overlooks the Ciron river (a tributary of the Garonne), which is responsible for the unique microclimate that gives rise to the famous "noble rot".

Rigorous management in the vineyard (sustainable viticulture, traceability, waste water treatment, etc.) and the cellar (new barrels, temperature control, etc.) reflect the harmony that has been found between traditional and modern methods. This is essential for making a wine worthy of First Growth status.

La Tour Blanche's style achieves a perfect balance between concentration and freshness, with impressive finesse and elegance. For all these reasons, Château La Tour Blanche unquestionably deserves its rank as the first of the First Growths in the 1855 classification.

| | |
|---|---|
| Area under vine | 40 hectares |
| Production | 35,000 bottles |
| Soil | Gravel with a clay-limestone subsoil |
| Grape varieties | 83% Sémillon, 12% Sauvignon, 5% Muscadelle |
| Barrel ageing | 16-18 months - New barrels: 100% |
| Second wine | Les Charmilles de La Tour Blanche |

Director: Alex Barrau - Sales: Didier Fréchinet - Cellar Master: Philippe Pelicano

Château La Tour Blanche 33210 Bommes
GPS: Latitude: 44.543010 - Longitude: -0.348030
Tel. +33 (0)5 57 98 02 73 - Fax +33 (0)5 57 98 02 78
tour-blanche@tour-blanche.com - **www.tour-blanche.com**

# Le Week-End

LE WEEK-END DES GRANDS CRUS

BORDEAUX

## SATURDAY: WINE AND GASTRONOMY

### The Tasting

The Union des Grands Crus de Bordeaux is offering wine lovers a unique opportunity to taste over 120 grands crus at a venue in the heart of Bordeaux. You can meet and discuss with château owners and oenologists, who will be glad to pour the most recent vintage of their wine in bottle as well as another year of their choice.

### The Dinners

You can also enjoy a very rare privilege: sharing a meal in one of the most prestigious châteaux in Bordeaux with the owners. This is a wonderful opportunity to match wine and food in the wonderful tradition of the French way of life.

## SUNDAY: REST AND RELAXATION

Visit the famous vineyards of Bordeaux and enjoy lunch at a wine château thanks to bus tours leaving from Bordeaux. Numerous châteaux will open their doors. Golfers are also invited to take part in the Union des Grands Crus de Bordeaux Cup, a competition involving wine lovers and owners of grand crus.

*Grands Crus de Bordeaux*

## Le Week-End

Programme, Booking & prices:
www.ugcb.net

11th Week-end des Grands Crus: 4 & 5 June 2016 - 12th Week-end: May 2017

# "BORDEAUX GRAND CRU"

## BY RIEDEL

This glass, first created in 1959 by Claus Riedel in the handmade Sommelier collection, and by Georg Riedel in 1986 in its machine-made version Vinum, is not a design gimmick but a precision instrument, developed to highlight the unique characteristics of the great wines of Bordeaux. The large bowl brings out the full depth of contemporary wines made from Cabernet Sauvignon, Cabernet Franc and Merlot.

Modern vinification techniques enable wine-makers to concentrate the fruit to such an extent that young wines may seem one-dimensional, tannic and over-oaked if served in smaller glasses.

The Bordeaux Grand Cru glasses give breathing space to both young and more mature wines, unpacking the various layers of bouquet and delivering a full spectrum of aromas. On the palate, the texture of the wine - soft, silky, velvety - is intensified and the finish prolonged, gently blending acidity with supple, sweet tannins. This is a glass that showcases these majestically structured red wines in all their complexity and finesse.

RIEDEL
THE WINE GLASS COMPANY

www.riedel.com

# INDEX OF CRUS

**General Remarks**

The list of members belonging to the Union des Grands Crus dates from December 15, 2015. The updated list can be found at www.ugcb.net.

Please note that there is no classification for the wines of Pomerol.

Furthermore, seeing as the size of the crop varies from one year to the next, the production figures cited in this guide are only an indication, and represent an average annual figure. They also only relate to the *grand vin*. Likewise, the surface area mentioned reflects not the total size of the estate, but the area under vine.

The GPS coordinates are expressed in decimals.

In keeping with French law, the publishers cannot be held liable in instances of involuntary errors or omissions despite the considerable attention and quality control measures that went into producing this guide.
The guide is co-published by:

The Union des Grands Crus de Bordeaux
10, cours du XXX Juillet
33000 Bordeaux - France.
&
The éditions Féret
24 allées de Tourny
33000 Bordeaux - France

**Editors**
Union des Grands Crus de Bordeaux - *President*, Olivier Bernard - *Manager*, Jean-Marc Guiraud
Olivier Crombez

**Coordination**
Éditions Féret - *Manager*, Bruno Boidron - *Assistant*, Véronique Garrouste

**Cover design**
Studio Pomelo - Bordeaux
**Interior design**
Vinexia.fr - *Manager*, Lison Braastad

**Maps**
Martin Lavielle © 2013

**Translation**
Aquitaine Traduction - *Directeur*, Alexandre Rychlewski

Printed on February 2016 in the EU
Copyright February 2016